What Wears a Sock on its Bottom?

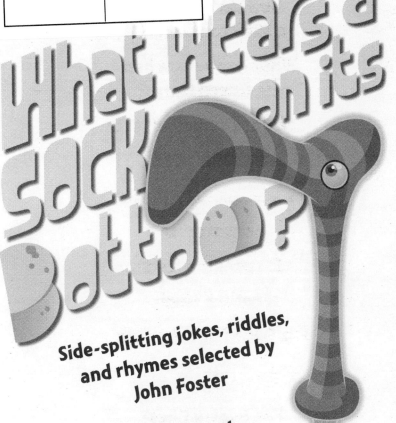

Side-splitting jokes, riddles, and rhymes selected by
John Foster

Illustrated by Mark Oliver

OXFORD
UNIVERSITY PRESS

OXFORD
UNIVERSITY PRESS

Great Clarendon Street, Oxford OX2 6DP
Oxford University Press is a department of the University of Oxford.
It furthers the University's objective of excellence in research, scholarship,
and education by publishing worldwide in

Oxford New York

Auckland Cape Town Dar es Salaam Hong Kong Karachi
Kuala Lumpur Madrid Melbourne Mexico City Nairobi
New Delhi Shanghai Taipei Toronto

With offices in

Argentina Austria Brazil Chile Czech Republic France Greece
Guatemala Hungary Italy Japan Poland Portugal Singapore
South Korea Switzerland Thailand Turkey Ukraine Vietnam

Oxford is a registered trade mark of Oxford University Press
in the UK and in certain other countries

British Library Cataloguing in Publication Data
Data available

ISBN: 978-0-19-275741-8
1 3 5 7 9 10 8 6 4 2

Printed in Great Britain
Paper used in the production of this book is a natural,
recyclable product made from wood grown in sustainable forests.
The manufacturing process conforms to the environmental
regulations of the country of origin.

CONTENTS

PANTS!

What wears a sock on its bottom?
Your leg.

Why do golfers wear two pairs of underpants?
In case they get a hole in one.

What do you get if you pull your knickers up to
your armpits?
A chest of drawers.

How did the pants feel after being ironed?
Depressed.

What do you call two robbers?
A pair of knickers.

Pants

Pants is what a dog does
When it's feeling hot.
Pants are what I wear
To cover up my bot.

Why?

Your hair is on top of your head.
You stand on the bottom of your feet.
So why don't you sit on your middle
When you sit on a toilet seat?

The Young Man from Australia

There was a young man from Australia
Who painted his butt like a dahlia
The drawing was fine,
The colour divine,
But the scent—ah! That was a failure.

A Pain in the Bum

Lavender Lottum
Has an itchy bottom.

Jeremy Styles
Has painful piles.

Theobald Thrum
Has a boil on his bum.

Dorothy Deer
Has severe diarrhoea.

Hermione Hants
Has ants in her pants.

Norman Nation
Has constipation.

And Verity Flickers
Has a wasp in her knickers.

The Boy
The boy stood on the burning deck,
His feet were full of blisters;
The flames came up and burned his pants
And now he wears his sister's.

When Mr Brown Went to Town
When Mr Brown went to town
People laughed 'cause his trousers fell down.
What made everyone point and stare
Was his lack of underwear.

The Young Curate of Sarem
There was a young curate of Sarem
Whose manners were quite harum-scarum.
He ran about Hants
Without any pants
Till the bishop compelled him to wear 'em.

WHAT DO YOU CALL A SMELLY GORILLA?

Roses Smell Sweet
Roses smell sweet
Honeysuckle too
Your dog smells revolting
And so do you!

What do you call a smelly gorilla?
King Pong.

What's frozen water?
Iced water.
And what's frozen tea?
Iced tea.
And what's frozen ink?
Iced ink.
I know you do!

Doctor, doctor, those pills you gave me
for BO are rubbish.
What's wrong with them?
They keep slipping out of my armpits.

I Once Met a Man From Hong Kong
I once met a man from Hong Kong
Who'd been jogging for twenty years long.
He was terribly sweaty.
He looked like a Yeti
And his feet had a terrible pong.

Common Scents
The porcupine may have his quills,
The elephant his trunk;
But when it comes to common scents,
My money's on the skunk.

All Alone
Here I sit all alone in the moonlight
Abandoned by women and men,
Muttering over and over,
'I'll never eat garlic again.'

What did the scientist say when he discovered how
to make a stinkbomb?
Eww—Reek—Aargh!

Humpty Dumpty Sat on a Bench

Humpty Dumpty sat on a bench.
Humpty Dumpty made a foul stench.
All the king's horses and all the king's men
Said they wouldn't sit next to Humpty again.

Why did Tigger smell?
Because he played with Pooh.

Knock, knock.
Who's there?
Sonia.
Sonia who?
Sonia shoe? I can smell it from here.

Cauliflower Nose

Cauliflower nose,
Cauliflower nose,
Your breath stinks
And so do your toes.

What's the smelliest game in the world?
Ping-Pong.

What do you get if you cross a chicken with a skunk?
Fowl breath.

Dirty Bertie Groves—a cautionary tale

This is the tale of Bertie Groves
Who never ever changed his clothes.
Whenever he went out to play
The other kids would run away.
'Bertie's coming!' they would yell,
Alerted by the pungent smell
Of Bertie's stained and tattered shirt
And Bertie's jeans spattered with dirt.
His sweaty socks gave such a stink,
It made the other children think
That the gunge between his toes
Must have begun to decompose,
And wonder what was lurking there
Beneath his unwashed underwear.

But Bertie Groves was unaware
Why other kids would sniff and glare
And leave him standing all alone
In his foul-smelling no-go zone.
Till he was caught out one morning,
When a storm, without a warning,
Ripped off all his tattered clothes,
Leaving dirty Bertie Groves
Standing naked in the street
With pools of water round his feet.

A man threw him a bar of soap,
Saying, 'Wash yourself, you little dope!'
And so, for quarter of an hour,
Bertie had a public shower.

A policeman, passing in his car,
Said, 'Bertie, you have gone too far.
To wash yourself is no disgrace,
But showering in a public place
Constitutes a serious crime.
But I will let you off this time,
If you can promise me and say
That you will change your clothes each day
And wash before you go to bed.'
Bertie Groves nodded his head,
Saying, 'Now I've clearly seen
How beneficial is hygiene.
From today I promise you
I'll change my clothes and shower too.'

I'M DYING TO TELL SOMEONE

Miss Chit-Chat

Beneath this stone Miss Chit-Chat lies.
Her gossiping days are done.
Her final words as she passed away were:
'I'm dying to tell someone.'

Reginald Hacking

Here lies the body
Of Reginald Hacking.
It was his cough
That bore him off.

Stanley Dyer

Here lies Stanley Dyer
Who said, 'I'm not ill.'
But he was a liar.

Mr Lee

Here lies a teacher Mr Lee
Who said, 'You'll be the death of me!'
And sitting at his desk one day,
He gave a sigh and passed away.

Constable Chest

Here lies the body
Of Constable Chest.
His heart made him
His last arrest.

A Miser

A miser lies beneath this stone
Stingy Timothy Wyatt.
He died one morning before ten
And saved a dinner by it.

Owen Moore

Owen Moore
Gone away
Owing more
Than he could pay.

A Heavy Penalty

Here lies a man who met his fate
Because he put on too much weight.
To over-eating he was prone
But now he's gained his final stone.

Did you hear about...?

Did you hear about the man who
swallowed a huge frog?
He croaked.

Did you hear about the man who was
convinced he was a candle?
He snuffed it.

Did you hear about the man who found everything
so funny that he couldn't stop laughing?
He was tickled to death.

Did you hear about the man who fell into his
computer's recycling bin?
He was permanently deleted.

Did you hear about the man who
forgot to renew his passport?
He expired.

Did you hear about the man whose sat nav
directed him to the cemetery?
He reached his final destination.

EGGSACTLY RIGHT FOR TENNIS

The Young Lady from Venice
There was a young lady from Venice
Who used hard-boiled eggs to play tennis.
When they said, 'It seems wrong.'
She remarked, 'Go along.
You don't know how prolific my hen is!'

A Tone-Deaf Old Person from Tring

A tone-deaf old person from Tring,
When somebody asked him to sing,
Said, 'I know it's odd
But I cannot tell *God
Save the Weasel* from *Pop goes the King*!'

A Thrifty Young Fellow of Shoreham

A thrifty young fellow of Shoreham
Made brown paper trousers and wore 'em.
He appeared nice and neat
Till he bent in the street
To pick up a penny and tore 'em.

Too Hot

When she bought some pyjamas in Cheltenham,
A lady was asked how she feltinem.
She said, 'Winter's all right,
But on a hot night,
I feel as if I'm going to meltinem.'

The Man from Bengal

There once was a man from Bengal
Who was asked to a fancy dress ball.
He murmured, 'I'll risk it
And go as a biscuit...'
But a dog ate him up in the hall.

An Executive Lady Named Claire

An executive lady named Claire
Never would comb her fair hair;
One day at a meeting
She heard a tweet-tweeting
And found two small birds nesting there.

LET'S GET AWAY FROM IT ALL

Where do sharks like to go for their holidays?
Finland.

Where do hot dogs go to chill out?
Iceland.

Where do ecologists go for
their holidays?
Greenland.

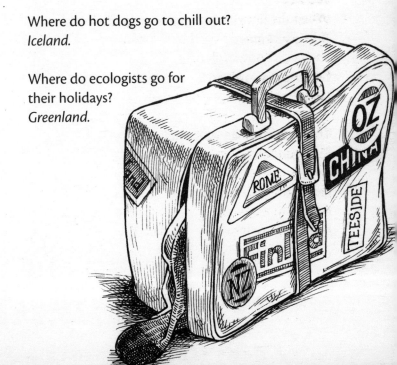

Where do optimists go for their holidays?
The Cape of Good Hope.

Where do enthusiasts go for their holidays?
New Zealand.

Where do the royal family go for their holidays?
Queensland.

Where do cups and saucers go for their holidays?
China.

Where do ramblers go for their holidays?
Rome.

Where do Egyptian mummies go for their holidays?
The Faroe Islands.

Where do wizards go for their holidays?
Oz.

Where do zombies go on holiday?
The Dead Sea.

Where do golfers go for their holidays?
Teeside.

THREE TWISTERS TO TWIZZLE YOUR TONGUE

Theophilus Thrapplethorn
Theophilus Thrapplethorn,
The celebrated thistle-sifter,
While sifting a sieve of unsifted thistles,
Thrust three thousand thistles
Through the thick of his thumb.
If Theophilus Thrapplethorn,
The successful thistle-sifter,
Thrust three thousand thistles
Through the thick of his thumb,
See that thou,
When thou siftest a sieve of thistles,
Do not get the unsifted thistles
Stuck in thy thumb!

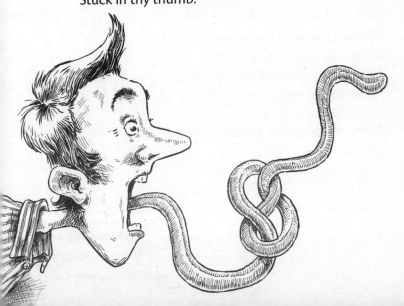

A Tutor Who Tooted a Flute

A tutor who tooted a flute
Tried to tutor two tooters to toot.
Said the two to the tutor,
'Is it harder to toot
Or to tutor two tooters to toot?'

A Lively Young Fisher Named Fischer

A lively young fisher named Fischer
Fished for fish from the edge of a fissure.
A fish with a grin
Pulled the fisherman in.
Now they're fishing the fissure for Fischer.

WAITER! THIS SOUP HAS A SMELL

Waiter! This Soup Has a Smell

Waiter! This soup has a smell
Reminiscent of brimstone from hell.
The taste is as foul
As a decomposed owl
And it looks like the slime on a well!

Apples

Apple crumble makes you rumble.
Apple cake makes you ache.
Apple pie makes you sigh.
Apple tart makes you fart!

Finding a Worm

Finding a worm in your apple
Is enough to make you squirm.
But what if you find in your apple
Is only one half of a worm?

Knock, knock
'Who's there?'
'Bernadette.'
'Bernadette who?'
'Bernadette *my* dinner.'

God Save Our Biscuit Tin

God save our biscuit tin,
Don't let the rats get in,
God save our tin.
And if they do get in,
Throw some rat poison in,
To save our biscuit tin,
God save our tin.

Granny Ate a Flea

One, two, three,
Granny caught a flea.
She salted it, and peppered it
And ate it for her tea.

A Young Boy Named Kidd

There once was a young boy named Kidd
Who ate twenty mince pies for five quid.
When asked, 'Are you faint?'
He replied, 'No, I ain't.
But I don't feel as well as I did.'

STUPID SIGNS

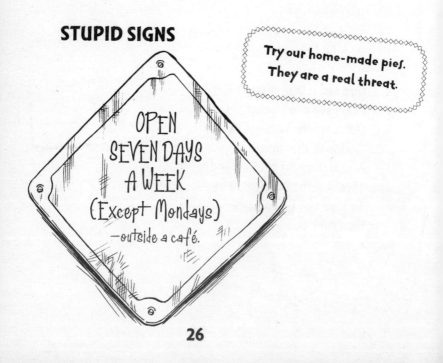

Try our home-made pies.
They are a real threat.

OPEN
SEVEN DAYS
A WEEK
(Except Mondays)
—outside a café.

NO
TRESPASSING
WITHOUT
PERMISSION

THE FARMER
ALLOWS WALKERS
TO CROSS THE FIELD
FOR FREE. BUT THE
BULL CHARGES.

IN CASE OF FIRE
DO YOUR BEST
TO ALARM THE
HALL PORTER.

WANTED—A MALE
WAITRESS

PRIZE WINNING
HANDMADE SAUSAGES.
ONCE TASTED YOU'LL NEVER
WANT ANOTHER
—outside farm shop.

OPEN 24 HOURS
(except 2 a.m. – 8 a.m.)
—on door of a pizza parlour.

All girls playing in Wednesday's hockey match will be pinned to the noticeboard.

Try our herbal remedies. You can't get better.

TOILET OUT OF ORDER PLEASE USE FLOOR BELOW
—on a toilet door in an office.

SHCOOL—Sign Painted On Road Outside A School.

CATTLE PLEASE CLOSE GATE.

BEWARE OF TRAINS GOING BOTH WAYS AT ONCE.

BARGAIN BASEMENT UPSTAIRS
—in a department store.

LADIES MAY HAVE FITS UPSTAIRS
—in a clothes store

WILL LADIES KINDLY EMPTY TEAPOTS, RINSE ROUND, AND, BEFORE LEAVING, STAND UPSIDE DOWN IN THE SINK.

29

IS READING ON THE TOILET MULTI-TASKING?

If a chicken has drumsticks, why doesn't it
have a drum?

If you lose your voice, where do you
start looking for it?

Why is it called the rush hour when
the traffic slows to a standstill?

If a flying saucer is an aircraft, does that
make a flying broomstick a witchcraft?

Why do they call it a TV set when you
only get one?

When they first invented the clock,
how did they know what time to set it to?

Is reading on the toilet multi-tasking?

How come abbreviation is such a long word?

What would a chair look like, if your
knees bent the other way?

Why is it called a missile; shouldn't
it be called a hittile?

If a tin whistle is made of tin, what is
a fog horn made of?

If a word was spelt wrong in a dictionary,
how would we know?

Why does your nose run and your feet smell?

Why is the third hand on a watch called
a second hand?

Do cats have to pay nine times more
for their life insurance?

Why do we say night falls, but day breaks?

How do 'Do Not Walk on the Grass' signs get there?

Why don't sheep shrink when it rains?

If a fly didn't have any wings, would it
be called a walk?

If all the world's a stage, where is
the audience sitting?

CLASSIC CROAKS AND MONKEY BUSINESS

Classic Croaks

What did the frog order at the fast food restaurant?
French flies and a diet croak.

Where do frogs sit?
On toadstools.

What happens if a frog's car breaks down?
It gets toad away.

Where do you take a frog with bad eyesight?
The hopticians.

What kind of sandals do frogs wear?
Open toad.

What did the bus driver say to the frog?
Hop on.

Where do frogs go to the toilet?
In the croakroom.

Why did the toad become a lighthouse keeper?
To have his own frog-horn.

What sort of films do frogs like?
Thrillers. Because they like croak and dagger stories.

Monkey Business
Where do monkeys buy their clothes?
Jungle sales.

How do you fix a broken chimp?
With a monkey wrench.

What's the first thing a monkey learns at school?
Its ape, b, c's.

What monkey looks like a flower?
A chimp-pansy.

Why did the monkeys go on strike at the circus?
They were fed up with working for peanuts.

Where do baby gorillas sleep?
In *ape-ri-cots*.

What do you get if you cross a monkey
with some egg whites?
A *meringue-utan*.

What is the smallest monkey in the
jungle called?
A *shrimpanzee*.

I FLEW WITH THE DINOSAURS

I've Got It!	by Penny Dropped.
I FLEW WITH THE DINOSAURS	by Terry Dactyl.
Rude Rhymes	by Ivor Cheek.
Daydreamer	by Edna Cloud.
How to Break a Window	by Eva Brickatit.
FLASHING WARNINGS	by Amber Light.
A Life of Crime	by Robin Banks.
Understanding Computers	by Mike Rochips.
The Explosive Business	by Dinah Mite.

PREHISTORIC CREATURES	by Dinah Soar.
Vegetable Gardening	by Rosa Cabbages.
Everybody's Got One	by Belle E. Button.
First Past the Post	by Rhoda Winner.
Unable To Sleep	by Eliza Wake.
Gone With the Wind	by Rufus Blownoff.
AT THE NORTH POLE	by I. C. Blast.
How to Build Igloos	by S. Kimo.
It's My Birthday!	by Felix Ited.
A Caged Bird's Story	by Ken Airey.

WHY DID THE DETECTIVE STAY IN BED ALL DAY?

Why did the detective stay in bed all day?
She was working undercover.

What did the habitual thief say in his defence?
*I'm a kleptomaniac, but I'm taking
something for it.*

Why did the burglar have a shower before leaving?
Because he wanted to make a clean getaway.

What do you call a robbery in Beijing?
A Chinese take-away.

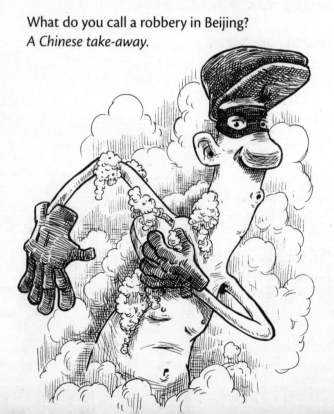

What happened to the burglar
who stole a calendar?
He got twelve months.

What do you get if you cross an ocean and a thief?
A crime wave.

Did you hear about the thief who stole
from a blood bank?
He was caught red-handed.

Why did the burglar carry a dustpan?
In case he had a brush with the law.

Why was the deaf burglar spared a prison sentence?
*Because you can't condemn someone
without a hearing.*

Why was the belt sent to jail?
For holding up a pair of trousers.

What do you call a burglar who fell
into a cement mixer?
A hardened criminal.

Did you hear about the thief who stole
prunes from the school kitchen?
He's still on the run.

Newsflashes

During the past few days three bicycles have been stolen. The police consider that a bicycle thief is at work.

A lorry load of wigs was stolen last night. Police are combing the area.

Two brothers have been arrested: one for stealing batteries and swallowing them, the other for stealing fireworks. One has been charged and the other was let off.

A MIRROR IS REPORTED TO HAVE BEEN STOLEN. THE POLICE ARE LOOKING INTO IT.

There was a break-in at the Open Door Baptist Church yesterday. The burglars are said to have entered through a rear window.

A van load of copies of a thesaurus was stolen from a book warehouse. Police are searching, examining, combing, scouring, checking the area for clues.

THE POLICE STATION TOILET HAS BEEN STOLEN. THE POLICE HAVE NOTHING TO GO ON.

FOR INDOOR OR OUTDOOR USE ONLY

A selection of ludicrous labels

On a microwaveable pudding:
Product will be hot after heating.

On a carton of milk:
Allergy advice—contains milk.

On a toilet brush:
Do not use for personal hygiene.

On a packet of peanuts:
Warning—contains nuts.

On a hairdryer:
Do not use while sleeping.

On a set of Christmas lights:
For indoor or outdoor use only.

On a bicycle:
Removing the wheel can influence the performance of the bicycle.

On the bottom of a soft drink bottle:
Open other end.

I'M A BUNGEE-JUMPING BOGEY

The Boy Stood on the Burning Deck
The boy stood on the burning deck
Picking his nose like mad;
He rolled them into little balls
And flicked them at his dad.

Old Mister Kelly
Old Mister Kelly
Had a pimple on his belly.
His wife cut it off
And it tasted just like jelly.

The Bogey Chant
Pick a bogey, flick a bogey
High up in the air,
Catch it on your tongue
And spit it over there.

It's Not Funny
If you want to kiss your honey
When her nose is runny,
You may think it funny
But it's snot.

The Black Cat and the White Cat

Oh! The black cat piddled in the white cat's eye.
The white cat said, 'Cor blimey!'
'I'm sorry, sir, I piddled in your eye.
I didn't know you was behind me.'

Under the Apple Tree

As I sat under the apple tree
A birdie sent his love to me.
And as I wiped it from my eye
I said, 'Thank goodness cows can't fly!'

I'm a Bungee-Jumping Bogey

I'm a bungee-jumping bogey
Leaping from your nose,
Past your belly-button
Right down to your toes.

I'm a bungee-jumping bogey
Covering you in grot and grime,
As I slither back and forth
Leaving trails of snot and slime.

SPRAINED MILK AND COWSLIPS

The cow stood on the hillside
The cow stood on the hillside,
Its skin as smooth as silk.
It slipped upon a cowslip
And sprained a pint of milk.

What romantic song do cows like best?
When I fall in love, it will be for heifer.

What do you call a silly man who is standing
in a cow pat?
An incowpoop.

What do you get if you cross a cow with a Frisbee?
Skimmed milk.

How do cows count?
With a cowculator.

Knock, knock
Who's there?
Cows go.
Cows go who?
Cows go moo, not who!

SLOW CATTLE CROSSING
NO OVERTAKING FOR
THE NEXT 100 YEARS

Where do cows go on holiday?
Moo York.

Where do cows go on a Saturday night?
The mooooooooooooovies.

What did one Highland cow say to another?
Och, aye, the moo.

What happens to cows in hot weather?
They give evaporated milk.

Where will you see a prehistoric cow?
In a moo-seum.

How do you make a milkshake?
By telling it a scary story

An Eccentric Old Person from Slough
An eccentric old person from Slough
Who took all his meals with a cow,
Said, 'It's quite uncanny,
She's so like Aunt Fanny.'
But he never would indicate how.

RHYME ME A RIDDLE

Answers on page 93

1. What is it that
   Goes over your head
   And under your hat?

2. East-West-North-South
   Hundreds of teeth
   No Mouth

3. Long legs, crooked toes.
   Glassy eyes, snotty nose.

4. Take season and seasoning,
   Add them together,
   And you'll spin through the air
   As light as a feather.

5. Although they have
   tongues, they do no talking.
   They have heels, but no
   toes, yet often go
   walking.

6. This will offer you a seat without ever talking.
Though it has a back and legs, it does no
walking.

7. The longer I stand and glow,
The shorter I grow.
I give light at night,
Until someone gives me a blow.

8. What has two hands, but no fingers,
A face, but cannot eat,
And moves at a regular pace
Although it has no feet?

9. What has a spine, but no bones,
Yet produces laughter and groans?

10. What hears without ears
And is able, too,
Without a mouth
To speak to you.

11. Where does sleep always come before yawning
And you have afternoon before morning?

What? How? Why?

1. What occurs once in a minute, twice in a moment, but never in a thousand years?
2. What starts with a T, ends with a T and is full of T?
3. How do you make varnish disappear?
4. How many peas are there in a pod?
5. Why should dieters avoid the letter C?
6. Why is an island like the letter T?
7. What is the centre of gravity?
8. Why is the letter 'g' scary?
9. Which three letters are full of power?
10. Which two letters are jealous?

A Well-Mannered Word

My last is the first of etiquette.
My second to last is the last of yet.
My third and fourth are together in lie.
My first is the leading letter of pry.
My second is the second in north and south
And found twice in tooth and once in mouth.
Solve this puzzle and you will see
How well-mannered a word can be.

What am I?

I am in destination and in mine,
In contain, initiate and fine,
In saving, but not in spend,
In begin, but not in end.
What am I?

A Point of Order
When does B come after U?

CHRISTMAS CRACKERS

What did Adam say on the day before Christmas?
It's Christmas, Eve!

What goes OH OH OH?
Santa walking backwards.

Who hides in the bakery at Christmas?
A mince spy.

What do you call Santa's little helpers?
Subordinate clauses.

Why are football managers like Santa's little helpers?
They are always getting the sack.

What is the best Christmas present in the world?
A broken drum. You just can't beat it!

What Santa Needs for Christmas

When in frosty midnight
He cruises through the air,
What Santa needs for Christmas
Is fur-lined underwear.

Good King Wenceslas

Good King Wenceslas walked out
In his mother's garden,
He bumped into a Brussels sprout
And said, 'I beg your pardon.'

While Shepherds Watched Their Turnip Tops

While shepherds watched their turnip tops
All boiling in the pot,
A lump of soot came rolling down
And spoiled the bloomin' lot.

A Christmas Booklist

Give Us a Kiss!	by Miss L. Toe.
Secrets of a Sleigh-Puller	by Rudolph Rednose.
Tunes Around the Tree	by Carol Singers.
Advice for Chimney Sweeps	by F. Christmas.
Traditional Decorations	by Holly Berry and Ivy Bush.
Follow That Star!	by A. Wiseman.
Christmas Party Foods	by Cherie Trifle.
Stocking-Fillers	by Candy Bars.
Too Many Chocolates	by Ivor Bellyache.
The Christmas Story Retold	by Bel Ringers.

QUEEN'S PARK STRANGERS AND DONCASTER RAVERS

What team do you get if you cross a royal
park with a group of foreigners?
Queen's Park Strangers.

What team do you get if you cross a royal residence
with a piece of cut glass?
Crystal Palace.

What team do you get by crossing a novelty
with an old fortress?
Newcastle United.

What team do you get if you cross a university
teacher with a type of sugar and a group of
partygoers?
Doncaster Ravers.

What team do you get if you cross a large
white bird, a large area of salt water and
a place which has a cathedral?
Swansea City.

What team do you get if you cross a
compass point with a piece of meat from a pig?
West Ham United.

What did the manager do when the
football pitch flooded?
He sent on the subs.

When do football pitches become triangles?
When someone takes a corner.

Why was Cinderella no good at football?
Her coach was a pumpkin.

What's the difference between the England football
team and a teabag?
A teabag stays in the cup longer.

Why was the school caretaker always picked
for the football team?
Because he was a good sweeper.

Golden Boots, Golden Boots
Golden boots, Golden boots,
Where have you been?
I've been up to London
To visit the queen.

Golden boots, Golden boots,
What did she say?
'I saw you sent off
On *Match of the Day*.'

CLASSROOM QUIPS

Knock, Knock
Who's there?
Teacher.
Teacher who?
Teacher self for a while. I'm off on holiday.

Teacher: Can you use the words defeat, defence and detail in a sentence?
Clever Trevor: *De feet of de dog went over de fence before de tail.*

Teacher: Recite your tables for me.
Clever Trevor: *Kitchen table, dining table, bedside table...*

Teacher: Name three collective nouns.
Clever Trevor: *Wastepaper bin, garbage bin, vacuum cleaner.*

Teacher: Can anyone tell me what a shamrock is?
Clever Trevor: *It's a fake diamond.*

Teacher: I hope I didn't see you looking at Simon's exam paper.
Clever Trevor: *I hope you didn't see me too.*

Clever Trevor: *Would you ever tell someone off for something they didn't do?*
Teacher: Of course not.
Clever Trevor: *That's good, because I didn't do my homework.*

Simon

Teacher: Can you say your name backwards, Simon?
Pupil: *No mis.*

Please French Teacher

Please French teacher
Listen to me.
I don't know the French
And I really need a 'Oui'.

Homework Howlers

The Equator is a menagerie lion running
round the Earth through Africa.

A magnet is something you find crawling
on a dead cat.

A Vacuum is a large empty space where
the Pope lives.

Napoleon was defeated at the
Battle of Waterloo Station.

THE WEIRD WORLD OF WORK
At the Job Centre

Clerk: *Here's a job with plenty of openings.*
Job applicant: *What is it?*
Clerk: *Hotel doorman.*

Clerk: *Here's a job that you can count on having lots of money.*
Job applicant: *What is it?*
Clerk: *Cashier.*

Clerk: *Here's a job with opportunities for promotion.*
Job applicant: *What is it?*
Clerk: *Advertising copywriter.*

Clerk: *Here's a job offering security.*
Job applicant: *What is it?*
Clerk: *Bodyguard.*

Clerk: *Here's a job that offers opportunities to climb the ladder.*
Job applicant: *What is it?*
Clerk: *Window cleaner.*

Clerk: *Here's a job with future prospects.*
Job applicant: *What is it?*
Clerk: *Astrologer.*

Clerk: *Here's a job where the sky's the limit.*
Job applicant: *What is it?*
Clerk: *Crane operator.*

Clerk: *Here's a job offering lots of training.*
Job applicant: *What is it?*
Clerk: *Fitness instructor.*

Clerk: *Here's a job offering long term employment.*
Job applicant: *What is it?*
Clerk: *Schoolteacher.*

Clerk: *Here's a job making loads of money.*
Job applicant: *What is it?*
Clerk: *Printer at the Royal Mint.*

Clerk: *Here's a job that's a real money spinner.*
Job applicant: *What is it?*
Clerk: *Croupier in a casino.*

What training do you need to be a garbage collector?
None. You pick it up as you go along.

Father: *My son wants to be a racing driver.*
Careers teacher: *Don't stand in his way.*

I Used to Work

I used to work as a butcher but I got the chop.

I used to work as a footballer but they kicked me out.

I used to work as an optician but I couldn't see eye to eye with my colleagues.

I used to work as a bouncer but they threw me out.

I used to work as a pilot but I left under a cloud.

I used to work as a chef but I made a hash of it.

I used to work as a dishwasher before the work dried up.

I used to work as a bank manager but I lost interest.

I used to work in a blanket factory but it folded.

I used to work as a historian until I realized there was no future in it.

NURSERY NONSENSICALS

Mary Was a Veggie
Mary was a veggie.
She wouldn't eat any meat.
She ate so many Brussels sprouts
What she did I can't repeat!

Hot Dog Buns
Hot dog buns!
Hot dog buns!
One a sausage, two a sausage,
Hot dog buns!

Hot dog buns!
Hot dog buns!
One with onions, two without,
Hot dog buns!

Mary Had a Little Gerbil
Mary had a little gerbil.
Which she dressed in
pretty blouses.
She also had a ferret
Which she put down
her dad's trousers.

Following the accident to Mr H. Dumpty, sitting on this wall is prohibited.
By order of the King's Men.

SHOOTING INCIDENT
Anyone who witnessed, or has information about, the shooting of Cock Robin, please contact Detective Chief Superintendent Eagle at Wing Police Station.

From: I. B. Strict (Headteacher)
To: Mary's mother
May I remind you that lambs are not allowed on the school premises. Please ensure that Mary does not bring hers to school in future.

MUMMY'S THE WORD

Wrapping Lessons

Although they didn't have first aid classes,
Egyptians were not dummies.
They knew how to put on bandages.
They learned how from their mummies.

Why was the mummy tense?
Because he had been wound up.

Why were Egyptian children confused?
Because their daddies were mummies.

Why don't mummies have any friends?
They are too wrapped up in themselves.

Why don't mummies like to rest?
Because they are afraid to unwind.

What does the notice on a mummy's garage door say?
Toot and come in.

What do you call two ancient Egyptian friends who
were buried in the same tomb?
Chummy mummies.

Why is it safe to tell a mummy your secret?
Because they will keep it under wraps.

Mummy, Mummy

Mummy, Mummy, what's a werewolf?
Be quiet, and comb your face.

Mummy, Mummy, what's a vampire?
Be quiet, and brush your fangs.

Mummy, Mummy, what's a ghost?
Be quiet, and go through that wall.

Mummy, Mummy, what's a witch?
Be quiet, and practise your spelling.

Mummy, Mummy, what's a mummy?
Be quiet, and stop picking at that bandage.

Mummy, Mummy, what's an elf?
Be quiet, and come back under the toadstool.

Mummy, Mummy, what's an alien?
Be quiet, and adjust your antennae.

Mummy, Mummy, what's a dragon?
Be quiet, and practise your fire-breathing.

YOU NAME IT!

Characteristically Named

Hugh Glue—he's stuck up.

Heather Feather—she's a lightweight.

Kate Late—she's never on time.

Guy Fly—he's a pest.

Lizzie Busy—she's always on the go.

Lance Prance—he's a show-off.

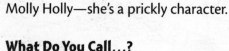

Tim Prim—he's always on his best behaviour.

Jane Brain—she's a know-it-all.

Joan Moan—she's always complaining.

Molly Holly—she's a prickly character.

What Do You Call...?

- a girl who is very hot: a sweaty Betty.
- a girl who is always cheerful: a jolly Polly.
- a girl with long legs: a leggy Peggy.
- a scatterbrained girl: a dizzy Lizzie.
- a girl with ringlets: a curly Shirley.
- a girl who is a busybody: a nosey Rosie.
- an uncooperative girl: a stroppy Poppy.
- a girl who always puts her clothes away: a tidy Heidi.
- a girl who is fond of practical jokes: a tricky Vicki.
- a girl who is sulky: a moody Judy.
- a girl who behaves foolishly: a silly Gilly.
- a girl who is always falling asleep in class: a dozy Posy.

The Name's The Same
(a riddle poem—Answer on page 93)

Why is Ronald Arnold
Like Brian Brain?
Why is Romeo Moore
Like Neal Lane?

Why is Thelma Hamlet
Like Edna Dean?
Why is Bertha Bather
Like Jane Jean?

Why is Clare Clear
Like Neil Line?
Why is Lydia Daily
Like Enid Dine?

Why is Miles Smile
Like Ruth Hurt?
Why is Norma Roman
Like Trish Shirt?

OPPORTUNITY KNOCKS

Knock, knock.
Who's there?
Boo.
Boo who?
Don't cry, it's only a joke.

Knock, knock
Who's there?
Norma Lee.
Norma Lee who?
Norma Lee I'd let myself in, but I've forgotten my key.

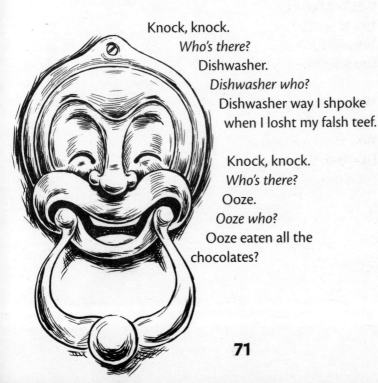

Knock, knock.
Who's there?
Dishwasher.
Dishwasher who?
Dishwasher way I shpoke
when I losht my falsh teef.

Knock, knock.
Who's there?
Ooze.
Ooze who?
Ooze eaten all the
chocolates?

Knock, knock.
Who's there?
Micky.
Micky who?
Micky won't fit. That's why I'm knocking.

Knock, knock.
Who's there?
My panther.
My panther who?
My panther falling down.

Knock, knock.
Who's there?
You.
You who?
Did you call?

Knock, knock.
Who's there?
Yul.
Yul who?
Yul soon see.

WHY DID THE CHICKEN CROSS THE ROAD?

Why did the chicken cross the road?
Because it had a death wish.

Why did the cow cross the road?
To get to the udder side.

Why did the pig run across the road?
Because it was a road hog.

Why did the bee cross the road?
To get to the buzz stop.

Why did the rubber
chicken cross the road?
*Because she wanted to
stretch her legs.*

Why did the hamburger cross
the road?
*To ketchup with the
French fries.*

Why did the skinhead cross the road?
He wanted to take a short cut to the barber's.

Why did Captain Kirk's chicken cross the road?
To boldly go where no chicken had gone before.

What did Shakespeare's chicken say when deciding
whether or not to cross the road?
To cross or not to cross—that is the question.

Why did the skeleton cross the road?
To get to the Body Shop.

Why did the comedian cross the road?
He did it just for a laugh.

Why did the hedgehog cross the road?
To see his flat mate.

Why did the squirrel cross the road?
To show the other squirrels he had guts.

AT THE SCHOOL WHERE TEACHERS ARE CREATURES

Dr Aardvark's Academy for Young Animals—Staff List

Head Creature: Mr Gorilla.

Deputy Head Creatures: Mr Shark, Mrs Vulture.

Bursar: Mr Money-Spider.

English creature: Mr Yak.

Maths creature: Mrs Adder.

Geography creature: Ms Turkey.

Biology creature: Mrs Lungfish.

PE creature: Mr Boxer.

French creature: Monsieur L'Escargot.

German creature: Herr Ing.

Woodwork creature: Mr Beaver.

Singing creatures: Ms Warbler, Ms Hummingbird.

Violin creature: Ms Fiddler-Crab.

IT creatures: Ms Mouse, Mr Web-Spinner.

RE creature: Ms Angelfish.

Cookery creature: Mrs Grub.

Parent-Creature Association Chairman: Mr Daddy-Long-Legs.

School Crossing Supervisor: Mrs Zebra.

MY UNCLE HAS A WOODEN LEG

My Uncle
My uncle has a wooden leg.
That's nothing. My uncle has a pine chest.

My uncle is pigeon-toed.
That's nothing. My uncle is pig-headed.

My uncle has a gold tooth.
That's nothing. My uncle has a silver tongue.

My uncle has carroty hair.
That's nothing. My uncle has cauliflower ears.

My uncle has green fingers.
That's nothing. My uncle has a Bluetooth.

Aunty Joan
When Aunty Joan became a phone,
She sat there not saying a thing.
The doctor said, shaking his head,
'You'll just have to give her a ring.'

We had a try, but got no reply.
The tone was always engaged.
'She's just being silly,' said Uncle Billy.
Slamming down the receiver enraged.

'Alas, I fear,' said the engineer,
Who was called in to inspect her,
'I've got no choice. She's lost her voice.
I shall have to disconnect her.'

The phone gave a ring. 'You'll do no such thing,'
Said aunty's voice on the line.
'I like being a phone. Just leave me alone
Or else I'll dial nine, nine, nine!'

I'VE GOT AN EXCUSE FOR YOU

Caller: *Trevor can't come to school today because he has an upset stomach.*
Teacher: *Who am I speaking to?*
Caller: *My father.*

Teacher: *Why weren't you here in time for registration?*
Trevor: *I was held up by the sign outside school which says Stop Children Crossing.*

Teacher: *Trevor, you should have been at school at nine o'clock.*
Trevor: *Why did something happen?*

Teacher: *Don't you understand the importance of punctuation?*
Trevor: *Yes, Miss. I always try to be on time.*

Teacher: *Why are you late for school again?*
Trevor: *It's not my fault if you ring the bell before I'm here.*

Teacher: *Trevor, you missed school yesterday, didn't you?*
Trevor: *Not a bit.*

Teacher: *Has your father been helping you with your homework?*
Trevor: *No, he did it all by himself.*

Teacher: *I've told you before not to come into school chewing gum.*
Trevor: *I'll stay at home and chew it there, if you'd prefer me to.*

Teacher: *How many millions of times do I have to tell you, Trevor, to stop exaggerating?*

Teacher: *Why weren't you at school yesterday, Trevor? I heard you were out playing football.*
Trevor: *That's not true, Miss, and I've got the cinema tickets to prove it.*

Four Good Reasons for Staying in Bed and Not Going to School

1. I haven't forged the note to say why I wasn't at school yesterday.

2. The head said she was going to ring Mum and I need to be in to intercept the call.

3. We're getting back our essays and Miss will want to know why mine is the same as Trevor's.

4. I've spent my dinner money on sweets, so I won't be able to have any dinner.

Top Ten Excuses For Not Handing In Your Homework

1. My baby sister was sick all over it.

2. I dropped it in the bath.

3. The dog ate it.

4. We were burgled and the burglar took it.

5. I was opening the window and it blew out.

6. My cousin made it into a paper aeroplane and someone hijacked it.

7. It was on the dining room table and I spilt gravy over it.

8. My mum used it to light the fire.

9. My dad picked it up and took it to work in his briefcase.

10. My sister's boyfriend's a magician and he made it disappear.

WHAT A LOT OF NONSENSE!

Johnny Went to Church One Day

Johnny went to church one day.
He climbed up in the steeple.
He took his shoes and stockings off
And threw them at the people.

On Top of Spaghetti
On top of spaghetti, all covered in cheese,
I lost my poor meatball when somebody sneezed.

It rolled off the table, and onto the floor,
And then my poor meatball rolled out of the door.

It rolled into the garden, and under a bush,
And then my poor meatball was nothing but mush.

The mush was as tasty, as tasty can be,
And early next summer, it grew into a tree.

The tree was all covered in beautiful moss,
It grew lovely meatballs and tomato sauce.

So if you eat spaghetti, all covered in cheese,
Hold on to your meatball and don't ever sneeze.

There Was a Young Student from Crete
There was a young student from Crete
Who stood on his head in the street.
He said, 'It is clear
That while I stand here,
I shall have to shake hands with my feet!'

Things You've (Probably) Never Seen
A shoe box
A salad bowl
A door catch
A coal scuttle
A bus trip
A hair slide
A nose dive
A sausage roll.

GIVE IT A MISS

Georgy Porgy
Georgy Porgy shouted 'Hi!'
To a girl as she passed by.
'Give me a kiss. Don't be shy.'
'Give you a kiss? I'd rather die!'

He Spoke the Truth
'Your teeth are like the stars,' he said
And pressed her hand so white.
He spoke the truth, for like the stars
Her teeth came out at night.

A Memorable Miss

I remember—I remember well,
The first girl that I kissed.
She closed her eyes. I closed mine.
And then—worst luck—we missed!

The Valentine

It sent a shiver down my spine
When I received a valentine
Saying, 'I think you're divine,'
'Cause it was signed from Frankenstein.

A Romantic Stroll
They strolled down the lane together.
The sky was studded with stars.
They reached the gate in silence
And he lifted down the bars.
She neither smiled, nor thanked him,
Because she knew not how.
For he was just a farmer's boy
And she a Jersey cow.
What happened to the two bedbugs that fell in love?
They were married in the spring.

Cinderella
Cinderella dressed in yella
Went downstairs to meet her fella.
On the way her panties busted—
How many people were disgusted?

Roses are Red
Roses are red.
Spiders are black.
Don't look now
But there's one on your back.

What happened to the two bedbugs that fell
in love?
They were married in the spring.

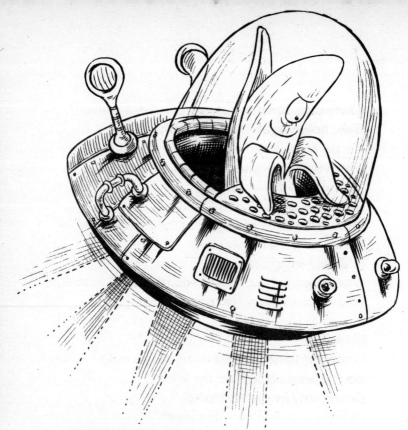

GOING BANANAS

What did the peel say to the banana?
Don't move. I've got you covered.

Why did the banana refuse to fight?
Because it was yellow.

Why didn't the banana snore?
To avoid waking the rest of the bunch.

Where can you find a banana's telephone number?
In the Yellow Pages.

What's the easiest way to make a banana split?
Cut it in half.

How did the banana burglar escape from the police?
He gave them the slip.

What kind of key opens a bunch of bananas?
A monkey.

Why aren't bananas upset when people make fun of them?
Because they have a thick skin.

What did one banana say to the other banana?
Nothing. Bananas can't talk.

What did the handsome young banana say to his girlfriend?
You appeal to me.

Why did the banana go out with a prune?
Beacause he couldn't find a date.

DID YOU HEAR ABOUT...?

Did you hear about the stupid tap dancer?
He fell in the sink.

Did you hear about the man who threw a
boomerang at a ghost?
It came back to haunt him.

Did you hear about the alien with five legs?
His jeans fit him like a glove.

Did you hear what happened to the man who
bought a paper shop?
It blew away.

Did you hear about the commuter who took
the five o'clock train home?
He had to give it back.

Did you hear what happened when a hyena
ate a box of Oxo cubes?
It made a laughing stock of itself.

TEN THINGS YOUR PARENTS AND TEACHERS WOULD NEVER SAY

Ten Things Your Parents Would Never Say

1. You can stay up as late as you like, it's only school tomorrow.

2. Of course I'll write a note saying you can't do PE because you say you're ill.

3. I know you didn't tidy your room, but here's your pocket money anyway.

4. Just leave the front door open, it'll let the fresh air in and the heat out.

5. Don't bother to change out of your school uniform, I can always wash it.

6. Don't worry about wiping your feet, the carpet's already dirty.

7. I don't have a tissue with me, just use your sleeve.

8. I'll write a note saying you couldn't do your homework because the match went to extra time.

9. Don't worry about what the teacher's written in your report, it's only her opinion.

10. Yes, I'll top up your mobile phone again, even though I did it a couple of days ago.

Ten Things Your Teacher Would Never Say

1. You're late, but don't worry. It's important you get plenty of sleep at your age.

2. You need energy, so there's a bar of chocolate for each of you at breaktime.

3. Keep your mobile phone switched on during lessons, in case someone needs to contact you.

4. It's your birthday so you can choose what you'd like to do all day.

5. It's too hot to work, let's go and sit in the shade and play charades.

6. Tell your mum I liked the story she wrote for your homework.

7. I realize none of you understood what I was saying, but you can all have a gold star for trying.

8. Meet me at the toy shop after school tomorrow and I'll buy you all a new toy.

9. Don't bother if your homework's late,
I'm going out and I won't have time to mark it.

10. I'm bored with this topic, let's tell some
jokes instead.

ANSWERS TO RIDDLES

Rhyme me a riddle
1: hair; 2: saw; 3: frog; 4: somersault; 5: boots; 6: a chair; 7: a candle; 8: a clock; 9: a book of jokes; 10: an echo; 11: in the dictionary.

What? How? Why?
1: the letter m; 2: a teapot; 3: Remove the r; 4: one p; 5: Because it makes the fat a fact; 6: Both are in the middle of water; 7: the letter v; 8: It turns host into ghost; 9: NRG; 10: NV.

A Well-Mannered Word
Polite

What Am I?
In

A Point of Order
When you steal its honey.

The Name's the Same (a riddle poem)
They're all anagrams

ACKNOWLEDGEMENTS

This collection Copyright © John Foster 2012
The following poems are Copyright © John Foster
and may not be reproduced without permission:

'A Pain in the Bum'
'A Well-Mannered Word'
'Aunty Joan'
'Cauliflower Nose'
'Constable Chest'
'Dirty Bertie Groves'
'Dr Aardvark's Academy for Young Animals—Staff List'
'Georgy Porgy'
'Golden Boots, Golden Boots'
'How Football Teams Are Created'
'Hot Dog Buns'
'Humpty Dumpty Sat on a Bench'
'Miss Chit Chat'
'My Uncle'
'Nursery Rhyme Notices'
'Reginald Hacking'
'Smelly Socks, Smelly Socks'
'Ten Things Your Parents and Teachers Would Never Say'
'The Bogey Chant'
'The Name's the Same'
'The Valentine'
'What am I?'
'When Mr Brown Went to Town'

At times, they involve other people to elicit reassurance, e.g.

> Edi: 'If I eat that I will get fat'.
>
> Response: 'Of course you won't.'

A repetitive cycle can be set up with the carer providing the safety routine. These exchanges allow Edi to rehearse eating disordered thinking, thereby reinforcing it. Ideally sidestep being invited to join in this dance.

> Response: 'I think you know that we all need food to live. The hospital have told me that I should not provide mindless reassurance so I will not say more.'

Disentangling the Meanings behind Food and Eating

The aim of treatment is to set the scene so that **the person with an eating disorder develops the skills and motivation to change**; relaxing their rule-bound eating and putting aside their safety behaviours.

Learning and memory is an active process involving brain growth and nerve synapse sprouting; malnutrition produces a reduction in brain growth factors and interferes with learning and active brain function. Thus, a vicious circle develops. When anorexia begins in adolescence, starvation interferes with the development of the 'social brain' and maturation of cognitive functioning. The result is that social, emotional and intellectual development is stunted and remains child-like. The capacity to reflect and the ability to step back and get an overview of emotions, thoughts and behaviours, all of which are essential to recovery, are impaired. Another trap is sprung.

Where anorexia develops at a later stage, Edi seems to regress to a much earlier level of development.

> When she was 23, at very low weight and very ill, my daughter frequently behaved as if she was about 3, with understanding and perceptions of around that age. GLS

> Your decision-making skills disappear. You have to ask for advice, reassurance and permission for everything. You can't interpret other people's reactions or emotions without guidance. You become totally dependent on others to function day-to-day, not just for nourishment, but to live. AC

Although it can be used for short periods to preserve life and improve brain function, forced feeding and attempts to change the eating disordered behaviour by coercion alone will not lead to permanent change. Unless these restricted, rule-bound patterns of eating are modified, they can become habitual and hardwired into the brain.

Therefore, helping someone with an eating disorder involves a balancing act: on the one hand giving the time and help needed to reach a point at which the individual has the motivation to explore and experiment with non-rule-bound eating and reduced safety behaviours; on the other hand, not letting malnutrition and symptoms interfere with brain function by causing brain cell death, disrupting reward pathways, and inhibiting learning and development.

The Body Fights Back – the Bulimic Trap

Extreme tension develops between rule-bound – or instrumental – eating and the physiological cues that control appetite. The body and brain desperately need nourishment to function effectively, and a series of mechanisms to increase appetite fight against malnutrition caused by the starvation. The strength of these innate mechanisms varies between individuals. It is possible that some individuals, genetically predisposed to anorexia nervosa, have a more loosely regulated system. The lifetime memory bank and

experience of food, eating and appetite is lost if abnormal eating behaviours persist for any length of time. Thus, the basic concepts of hunger and fullness have to be relearned and gradually trained to take over normal appetite control.

In some individuals the 'reward pathways' become so sensitive that, once eating restarts, it takes a while to shut off. A drive to overeat, with intense urges and cravings, emerges.

A variety of perverse eating behaviours arise when rule-bound eating is at war with the biology of appetite, e.g. picking/stealing foods and binge eating. The response to this drive, and the intense urges and cravings, will vary with the individual. For instance, in the restrictive type of AN, purging behaviours such as vomiting may not be part of the scene; while in AN binge/purge type it may enter the picture at an early or later stage. Chapter 12 focuses on helping to reduce bingeing and overeating behaviours.

B. Thinking about Changing Eating

Insight Using the Nutritional Risk Ruler

In Chapter 7, the use of a 'Readiness Ruler' to aid motivation to change is illustrated. Here, we use the same tool to discuss the balance between motivation to change and objective evidence of nutritional safety. The 'Nutritional Risk Ruler' gauges Edi's insight into the potential impact the illness plays on their medical health as well as their quality of life, both in the short and long terms. **The aim is to initiate a conversation discussing nutritional health.**

Nutritional Risk Ruler:

Unable to ensure nutritional safety   *Maintain full nutritional health*

0------1--------2------3-----4-----5------6------7-----8------9--------10

Compensatory or 'Safety Behaviours'

At times Edi takes food only to please and appease others – social cues; or in response to powerful appetite cues – overwhelming hunger; or in an attempt to cover their disordered eating behaviour. This 'non-rule-bound' eating causes high anxiety.

When my daughter, aged 23, developed anorexia, binge/purge type, she ate a good healthy meal across the table from me each evening. GLS

I would hate the thought of friends seeing me as weak, pathetic or appearance conscious, the usual eating disorder stereotypes. If ever I had to eat with people I would restrict rigorously beforehand. I would then attempt to eat as normally as possible at dinner and conceal my terror. Panic-stricken after a 'huge' meal, I would walk home (miles) and exercise and restrict the next day to compensate for my indulgence. AC

To cope with this distress, a variety of what are called 'safety' behaviours may develop, e.g. vomiting, misuse of laxatives, over-exercising, or thoughts to try to neutralise the distress which are found soothing, such as: '*Once I am free I will choose how I will eat*', or perhaps, '*Being made to eat doesn't count*', etc.

After she had eaten with me, she went upstairs to her bedroom, saying she wanted to watch TV. On the way to her bedroom she visited the bathroom to get rid of everything she had eaten. GLS

Later on in my illness, although I still wouldn't feed myself adequately, I started to accept food from my parents. Giving food to myself was too indulgent; I was worthless and undeserving. Accepting food from others was different – the choice was removed and the guilt after eating was alleviated slightly. AC

As they reduce the anxiety caused by eating, these safety behaviours can quickly become reinforced and habitual.

ACTION POINT

Plotting Nutritional Risk

1. Using the Ruler above, start by asking how Edi would rate their current ability to manage their own nutritional well-being. Mark this on the Ruler.

2. Follow up this score with reflections and further questions, for example:

   - *Why that score?*

   - *Why that score rather than 0? **(This can often elicit motivational statements as it asks for thoughts and behaviours that are in a positive change direction.)***

   - *What would have to happen to be at 10?*

   - *What help would be needed to get to 10?*

     Here, you are setting the scene for, and encouraging, 'change' talk.

3. Edi may give themselves a high score, at variance with your judgement. If this occurs, ask whether you can illustrate *your* position using the same tool. *'Would you mind if I use the same Ruler to mark where it seems you are from my perspective?'*

4. Explain calmly with observations and feedback why you have given that score:

   - *'I would put you on a 4 because I see that you are very sensitive to the cold – when I go up to your room you have extra heat on.'*

   - *'The doctor told us that your blood pressure and pulse rate are very low.'*

- *'The examination came up red on some of the risk factors on his chart.'*

Avoid sounding critical or judgemental. Use first-person observations: *'I notice . . .'*, or third-person statements: *'The doctor says . . .'*. Avoid *'You this or that . . .'*, which sound accusatory.

Or,

- *'I notice that you have given yourself a higher score than I have been able to do. What do you think you would be able to do to show me that I am being too pessimistic? How could you show me that you can take care of yourself and that your score merits being higher?'*

5. Given any discrepancy between objective and subjective scores, ask Edi how much others (including yourself) will be needed to safeguard their health.

- *'It is up to you how you manage your nutritional health. You are the only one who can decide this.'* Whenever possible emphasise Edi's freedom and ability to choose. This helps increase motivation.

6. As well as emphasising choice, highlight that your help is available when she or he is ready.

- *'If there is anything I can do to help you improve your nutritional health, then please say. I am more than happy to assist and support you in any way that I can – both practically and emotionally. I trust, that when you would like help, you will ask me. The offer is always open.'*

Society's Responsibility for Nutritional Safety

Ideally enough time will be available to gently raise awareness with Edi of the consequences, to life and health, of inadequate nourishment. Ideally, enough time will be available to work towards motivating Edi to think about, initiate and maintain changing eating behaviour. Ideally, enough time will be available to raise Edi's self-esteem and confidence that he or she can succeed through all setbacks encountered. However, unfortunately there are situations – for instance when an individual's current medical state is perilous or highly unstable – when the necessary time or resources are not available.

ACTION POINT ➡️

Plotting Medical Risk

1. You may want to use the Maudsley BMI risk chart on the IOP website www.eatingresearch.com in the section for general practitioners to plot Edi's BMI. Maybe involve Edi in this? 'Let's read out where you fall on this chart.'

2. You may want to have a conversation about the implications of medical risk as judged from both the BMI banding chart and also from other aspects of medical function from the 'Risk Assessment in Anorexia Nervosa' chart, also found on the website www.eatingresearch.com, in the section for professionals.

You may want to look at standard growth and development charts: www.cdc.gov

A BMI of below 13.5kg/m² is a marker of high medical risk, and inpatient treatment is recommended. If risk is in these areas, doctors and lawyers consider using the Mental Health Act (see Chapter 6) to ensure safety. The possibility of using the Mental Health Act needs to be discussed with Edi in addition to the dangers and mortality risk at this low weight. It is reasonable to open a discussion about this as, unfortunately, anorexia nervosa has the highest mortality rate of any psychiatric disorder. Both professional and lay carers should discuss the necessity of using the MHA in a non-personalised way. It is a care pathway that has to be followed when needed, as part of good practice, and is not used to bully or threaten. As always, gentle persuasion using motivation through discussion is preferable to confrontation and admission to hospital completely against Edi's wishes. Although, when there is high risk, eating becomes the top priority.

ACTION POINT ➡

Plotting Medical Risk *continued . . .*

3. Using the BMI risk chart, combined with scores (yours and Edi's) from the 'Nutritional Risk Ruler' task, calmly explain the situation to Edi. Here is an example:

- *'It looks as if it is difficult for you to be aware of your own nutritional health. If we put in some of the objective observations about your body function there are indications that your health/growth and development are in jeopardy. Yet you are unable to feel this. The evidence for this is the large discrepancy between your score and mine on the Nutritional Risk Ruler. Look – your score is here, but I've marked you here. It looks as if you are being tricked by the eating disorder into thinking that there is nothing wrong and that you are OK. That is not the case. I am very worried, and need extra help.'*

Your responsibility to safeguard Edi's well-being needs to be calmly explained. Remember the St Bernard dog behaviour.

ACTION POINT ➤

Explaining Society's Role

'If your illness means that you cannot be responsible for your nutritional health, then I have a duty of care to safeguard your life. In court I would be considered responsible for your health, and negligent if I just stood by and did nothing.'

'Society also holds itself responsible for safeguarding nutritional health in people with eating disorders. That's why there are statutory rules such as the Mental Health Act.'

'If we use this line to represent the degree of responsibility that society needs to take for your health, where do think you are on this line?'

0------1--------2------3------4-------5---------6-------7------8---------9--------10

No help needed from society	Help needed from society
No risk to health	Health is at risk
No need for others to ensure nutritional safety	Mental Health Act is needed to ensure nutritional safety

'Why that score rather than 10?'
'What would have to happen for you to be at 0?'
'What help will you need until you can get to 0?'

If the eating disorder is severe it will be difficult for Edi to have a realistic perspective. The conversation may go like this:

> 'You have told me that you do not think you need help and that you can care for your nutritional safety. I understand that is how it "feels" to you. However that's in contrast to the objective facts which are . . . Let us try to think of the least restrictive way we can work within the rules set down by society. I would prefer us to succeed at home rather than go to hospital. I would prefer it if you could make the plan. What help might you need from me to do that? What other help might you need?'

C. Creating Distance from Eating Disorder Rules

The following section illustrates the type of processes used in therapy to increase the motivation to move away from rule-bound eating. It may be helpful for you to be mindful of these and to experiment with using this sort of approach.

(1) Distance through Conversation

In order to foster change it is necessary to build a non-eating disorder identity. The goal is to develop a range of more flexible, adaptive perspectives. The first stage in progress is to understand ambivalence.

- What are the pros and cons of the status quo?

- What are the pros and cons about trying to change?

- What are the pros and cons of having a non-eating disorder identity and lifestyle?

Such a conversation might go like this:

skills-based learning for caring for a loved one

'After getting into such a habit and routine with your pattern of eating, you must be terrified about how you will be able to break this pattern of behaving.'

'Your appetite system may be disrupted by the eating disorder. The effort needed to relearn how to attain normal nutritional health will be immense; maybe you think it would be too difficult for you?'

- **This reflection over-emphasises the difficulty of change. The therapist is speaking in the role of a 'Devil's Advocate', indicating how very difficult change might be. The natural reaction to such a stance is for the person with the eating disorder to come back with a reply from the opposite point of view, i.e. to state that it might not be so bad, Edi may be able to do something . . .**

The following is the type of reply you sometimes elicit from Edi (though perhaps not in these words).

'No, I am not terrified that I can't do it because I've made some changes already. For example, I used to use food either to punish or to reward myself. I'd only allow myself to eat depending on how I judged how the day had gone. Now I'm able to make sure I can eat no matter what the day has been like. Also, I found it difficult to eat because my judgement of hunger was unreliable. In the past I would always choose a non-calorific drink but now I am replacing these with yoghurt drinks or smoothies to increase my calorie intake. I've learnt that my signals of hunger and my feelings trick me.'

The 'Devil's Advocate' stance may also be used to examine what is positive for Edi about their illness, and simultaneously raise questions in Edi's mind.

'There must be things that you find positive about poor nutritional health or would be afraid to lose if you tried to attain better nutritional health?'

- The aim of these questions is to develop awareness of discrepancy and dissonance. Challenging the eating disorder in this way brings with it some sort of distress – which may be expressed in a variety of individual ways – **but this emotional charge, whether through explosive rages, screaming or roaring, is essential for motivation**.

Such a conversation sets the negative aspects of the illness against the positive by building up discrepancy. It is helpful if you can listen to those aspects of the eating disorder seen as positive to Edi. Beware of prematurely stepping in; rubbishing and invalidating what is said. Thoroughly explore what is meant so that you can see whether there are other ways in which Edi can attain his or her illness's perceived benefits.

Box 11.1 amalgamates thoughts expressed by many eating disorder sufferers; the pros (reasons as to why a sufferer may be reticent to give up their illness) and the cons (negative, dismissive feelings towards the eating disorder). After reading the examples, maybe you will be able to appreciate how some of the comments are relevant to the individual under your care?

BOX 11.1 Thoughts about Eating Disorder

Reasons to Stay with the Eating Disorder

- *Makes people listen to me.*

- *Makes me feel that people are concerned about me.*

- *I am cared for and looked after. Everything feels so safe.*

- *I get to spend more time at home with Mum and Dad. I don't have to do grown-up things like go to university or move away from home.*

- *Sense of achievement/satisfaction from holding off eating.*

- *Food is a treat: (a) at the end of the day – save up for dinner time; (b) unusual foods seem too indulgent; (c) thought of it helps to pass the time.*

- *I actually like a lot of the things I eat now and feel annoyed if I 'make myself' eat different things. Also feel bewildered by choice in supermarkets, etc., so easier to go with what I know.*

- *Sense of gluttony.*

- *The guilty feelings and sense of failure I have after I have overindulged are just too terrible.*

- *Makes me feel different/special.*

- *Gives me influence over others.*

- *Fear of adult relationships and responsibilities.*

- *Males might find me attractive if I put on weight and look 'normal'. I don't want that. Anorexia is my defence mechanism. I want to look like I do now.*

- *Fear that I'll get better and nothing will have changed and the old dissatisfactions, injustices and problems will still be there, waiting for me.*

- *Feel I have sunk so low there's not much worse.*

- *It was a secret before but everyone knows now so what's the point in trying?*

- *It fills up all my thoughts and takes all my energy. If I give up the illness, my life will be empty. I'll have nothing.*

- *Worry that my worst fears will be realised – i.e. proof that if I do start enjoying eating and drinking again, and put on weight, I won't be able to continue once I reach a normal weight and will have to cut everything out again – it's easier just to never get used to it as I no longer miss most things.*

- *It's what I'm used to now – can't imagine anything different.*

- *My eating disorder has taken me out of life for so long. Compared to everyone else my age, I'm so young. I have lost too many years to catch up on now. It's too daunting.*

- *Fear of setting a precedent and raising others' expectations. People will expect me to do 'normal' things like socialise and have a boyfriend. This terrifies me.*

- *Everyone will notice my weight gain and then I will feel under pressure to achieve recovery. What if I then fail? People will watch me and talk about it – this will make eating in public very difficult.*

Reasons to Move Away from the Eating Disorder

- *I've lost so many friends through my illness. I've driven away my family too.*

- *The illness makes me selfish – I don't have the time or brain space to think or care for others.*

- *I will not be able to have a family of my own if I stay with my anorexia.*

- *I've lost my freedom. I'm not allowed to do anything or go anywhere by myself. Everyone watches my every movement. No one gives me any privacy.*

skills-based learning for caring for a loved one

- *I've missed out on so much because of you – holidays, birthdays, parties, Christmas, etc.*

- *The illness makes me lie and deceive people. I become a horrible person when it's with me.*

- *I will never be able to achieve my dream job as a vet unless I give up my eating disorder.*

- *I'm not allowed to do the things I love any more – like swimming and cross-country running.*

- *My bones are already thin. I am liable to develop osteoporosis at a young age.*

Encouraging Edi to discuss openly his or her beliefs as to the possible benefits and 'pitfalls' of their illness is a useful exercise. However, you may be disappointed – Edi will always be in two minds . . .

'I am terrified about osteoporosis.' But then she or he may say, *'I do not want to gain any weight.'*

Or, *'The disability caused to me by spraining my ankle made me think of what it could be like to be immobilised with osteoporosis.'* But then, *'I see those people who have recovered from anorexia as fat.'*

These mixed messages and confusing thoughts can be difficult to tolerate. Carers may be tempted to step in to cover up, reach a conclusion, and somehow make things easier for the sufferer. Try to avoid stepping in to reassure; rather validate how confusing it must be.

For Edi, this is an uncertain and distressing time; once adamant, now intermittently doubtful, that their illness is of benefit. Edi's feelings will swing rapidly; they may have periods where positivity, looking to the future and scathing comments about the eating disorder shine through. Then will come the 'negative cloud'; arguments about meal size, comments about excessive fat, low self-esteem, despair, etc. The change can be rapid – literally minutes. They are in turmoil. This is immensely frustrating as a carer but try to keep in mind that *the energy caused by the distress of dissonance will eventually help promote change*.

> I would sometimes have a really positive conversation with my Mum; about the future, my plans, holidays, how I could get through the illness, my desire to give it up, etc. Then, it would be time for a meal or a snack. My world narrowed – I wouldn't be able to see past the calories and the image of me ballooning. My brain whirred with plans as to how I was going to get rid of the food afterwards, how would I compensate? It would be so frustrating; the sudden snap change – I had just been thinking so positively. Everything had seemed possible, what happened? AC

(2) Distance Through ABC

ABC (Antecedents, Behaviour, and Consequences) is an important theoretical tool used in psychology to understand behaviour. To change any behaviour, it is essential to consider **Antecedents**, i.e. the triggers or the internal and external setting conditions that promote the **Behaviour**, and the **Consequences** of the behaviour – what positive internal or external effects follow from the behaviour or what punishing effects are averted or avoided. The theory is that behaviour is triggered by events, and that humans continue with behaviours that produce some sort of reward for the individual whether towards reaching a goal, or gaining personal attention.

Reading the list in Box 11.1 'Reasons to Stay with the Eating Disorder', is it possible to work out what the **As** are to make people want to follow eating disorder rules? These are a few – you may think of more.

- Emotional triggers: feeling unworthy, unhappy, inadequate and anxious.

- Thinking triggers: thoughts in which food has additional or unusual meaning.

Changing the Antecedents

Carers can promote conditions in the home or community that foster eating by ensuring the atmosphere at home is as warm as possible. Criticism and hostility only serve to increase anxiety, which makes eating difficult. *No matter how frustrating mealtime behaviour is*, remain calm – if you get anxious or angry, Edi becomes even more anxious and angry, and finds it more difficult to eat. She or he will use their anger/anxiety as an excuse to leave the table and refuse food. Set the scene so that social eating can be as pleasant as possible, perhaps think beforehand of neutral topics to discuss at the table (current films at the cinema or

FIGURE 11.3   ABC Functional Analysis: Undereating

Internal triggers
- Anxious
- Unsafe
- Avoid emotions
- Avoid others
- Low esteem

Antecedents*

External triggers
- Criticism, hostility

Rule-driven eating

Positive effects
- Special skill
- Achieve focus and goals
- Concern others

Consequences

Negative effects
- Criticism and concern from others
- Consequences of starvation (preoccupation with food, physical disability)

Note: * Antecedents may be perceived or actual – even remarks intended as expressing interest or care may be misinterpreted as critical or hostile by Edi.

sports news for example) or tell the family about your day or encourage another family member to speak of their activities. No matter how mundane the chat is, it will act as calming background noise for Edi. If an uncomfortable or tense silence develops, think about having some low-volume tranquil music playing in the background before you all sit to start the meal. Maybe instruct one family member to read out crossword clues, for example, as a distraction or talk about activities planned for after the meal or at the weekend. If you have time and energy, go the extra mile for attractive table settings or maybe eat outside if the weather is fine.

Changing your Behaviour, to Change Edi's

To overcome the eating disorder-thinking triggers, assertiveness skills are needed. These include being:

- **Calm**. Be clear and firm when stating what you want to see happen and reminding the individual what has been agreed.

- **Compassionate**. Acknowledge how difficult it is for Edi to see any other perspective and to want to change now, with food in front of them. However, remind them that your perspective differs. Be prepared to repeat patiently what you want to happen.

- **Caring and concerned**. Offer to help the other person in any way you can. Ask what Edi thinks might help.

- **Coaching**. Talk Edi through how their mind focuses on micro-detail and 'the now'. Explain that, as an observer, you are able to see the bigger picture and the future. Entering into a discussion about the detail of the diet is not helpful. People need to eat to live. You are interested in promoting life quality. That is your bottom line. You may need to repeat this message calmly, kindly and persistently.

- **Not colluding**. Do not get drawn into reassurance-giving, e.g. *'This will make me fat won't it?'* Try to keep to neutral discussion topics – do not join in eating disorder talk about food, weight or shape.

Calm, coaching comments to keep the eating pace going are helpful:

'It is not helpful if you focus on the detail of what sort/what calories/what amount . . .'

'Let's stick to the plan – we are interested in nutrition for health and quality of life.'

'What is more helpful is to keep your eye on what we want to achieve in terms of your life story.'

'I would like your life to be more than eating.'

'Let's zoom out to connections to people and the world rather than being stuck on nutritional basics.'

'I know that there is more to you than food and weight. Let's move on and get there.'

Changing the Consequences

Both internal and external consequences need to be considered.

Internal consequences: Extreme anxiety is the commonest consequence for Edi when his or her individual eating disorder rules are not obeyed. A pattern of compulsive safety behaviours may develop after the event. As outlined above these include: exercising, vomiting, purging, reassurance-seeking and calculating eating-disordered thoughts (i.e. plans to cut back later).

Helping Edi to master the intense surge of anxiety which occurs with the sensation of fullness *without* using one of these strategies is a core part of the process. Therefore, when helping to coach Edi into improving their nutritional health, remember it does not stop when the meal is over. Planning follow-up distracting activities can be helpful. A joint conversation, jigsaw puzzle, crossword, looking through a book or photo album, a gentle walk round the garden or up the road, watching a brief news update, film or television programme are some of the things that can interrupt these compulsions.

Such a distraction should ideally last for about 30 minutes after a meal (15 minutes after a snack). After this period of time, Edi will feel less physically full and thus will be more unlikely to initiate a compensatory safety behaviour.

Some sufferers may be too tense, angry and resentful after a meal to concentrate or participate in a joint activity. This fury may stem from eating but also from your presence preventing them from performing a safety behaviour. The sufferer may, and probably will, direct their rage onto you. Maybe try and encourage them to release their frustrations some other way – punching a pillow or a cushion, drawing, painting or writing about how they feel. A post-meal food diary may help Edi to express their hatred and dissatisfaction with themselves and their life through words. How did that meal make them feel and why? Remember that many, if not all, eating disorder sufferers lack emotional intelligence and identifying and vocalising feelings presents a considerable challenge.

> '*I would like to help you through this tough, post-meal, anxiety. I know how agonising it is for you to resist your compulsive drive to . . . Remember that we set a goal of staying with the challenge for 30 minutes. How can I help? Shall we walk round the block and you can tell me about your day?*'
>
> '*I can see how distressed that meal has made you feel. I know you are angry and anxious. Maybe if you cannot explain or talk to me about your inner thoughts, then you could write them down? Just getting them out, somehow, may help you to feel less full physically by lifting some of the emotional burden you are currently carrying.*'

External consequences: It is important that rule-driven eating is not praised or seen as appropriate.

The following example may help to illustrate this by describing how to analyse 'rewarding' or 'non-rewarding' responses to Edi's behaviours:

Tania's mother, Sue, would sit with Tania throughout a meal and ensure that she had finished.

(This is a good example of giving attention to the behaviour of the normal part of her daughter – the part that knows that it is necessary to eat to live.)

After the meal Tania would retreat to her room in floods of tears. Sue would follow her daughter and hug her and try to comfort her.

(This might be seen as rewarding and/or reinforcing anorexic behaviour by giving it attention – it is the 'anorexic minx' that is distressed by eating, not the normal part.)

Sue and her husband David analysed the situation. They decided that Sue should ignore the post-meal tears. They decided to approach Tania when she was in a calm state at their next meeting and offer to spend some time together after a meal to help distract her from her distress, for example a walk around the block, watching a TV programme, etc.

Thus after the meal Sue reminded Tania that they were going to have a walk. Sue noticed that Tania's tears did not last for very long if she ignored them. She also noticed that Tania gradually opened up more during their time together.

Remember that these kinds of rewards, such as your attention and care, are the most potent motivators, e.g.

'When we finish this meal, let's do more of the collage/weaving/ scrapbook together' or 'When you finish this, let's go for a walk together.' 'It is tough to pull away from pain, but let's try to put it away for now. Imagine it in your big toe for now while you and I play Scrabble/watch that programme . . .' Or . . .?

(Through discussion, each family will find different solutions and ideas depending on the individuals involved.)

D. Implementing Eating

Choices

There is no choice about whether to eat or not. However, choice can be given about **where** to eat a meal or snack: '*Would you prefer to have a snack in the garden or inside? Or, what about taking a picnic out for lunch?*' Within boundaries, **when** to eat can also be flexible: '*Would you prefer to have a snack at 3 or 4 o'clock?*' And, so can with *whom*. Additionally, Edi has yet another choice: **what** to eat (note – what rather than *if* to eat). Suggest two or three alternatives: '*Would you prefer a yogurt, toast or a smoothie for a snack?*'

Working to Change Rule-Bound Eating Behaviour

It is important that families work together on issues related to eating. This is not easy as different personality styles can favour contrasting approaches. Also, some family members may have their own issues around food, clouding matters further. With media focus on body image, shape, weight and 'healthy eating', many people regularly follow diets or 'watch what they eat'. It is more difficult to take a non-biased perspective if any family member holds extreme shape and weight concerns. Additionally, supermarket food packaging and branding is geared towards the 'calorie conscious' – '*only 100 calories per bar!*', '*reduced fat!*', '*99 per cent fat free*'. Such clearly labelled food items are unhelpful to have in kitchen cupboards when Edi is around and, are certainly not suitable for a weight-increasing diet. A family discussion and joint decision need to take place about where such products should be kept and whether labels should be stuck over the nutritional information on these foods, etc. Additionally, discussion needs to focus on the eating behaviours of other family members. Maybe someone else other than Edi has a behaviour that requires challenging? It is difficult as there is a fuzzy line between what counts as an eating disorder symptom and what is 'normal' eating behaviour. However, an eating disorder thrives on splits and divides within a family, so what is important is a consistent, joint family approach.

Planning

Once Edi has resolved mixed feelings about change and has reached the stage of Action (see Chapter 7), you can then help and support in making detailed implementation plans.

Remember that Edi should have been aware before reaching this stage that your support and help was, and will be, always available. She or he may not have been ready for it previously, but on reaching the stage of Action you can start planning and discussing putting change into place TOGETHER. It is important to bear in mind that setbacks are often encountered as commitment to change, and energy, fluctuate. The eating disorder may be renewed, with a return to an earlier stage of the illness (see Chapter 7) so, be prepared for this.

(1) Planning – Discussion Time

It is important to go through this planning stage in great detail. Edi needs to feel safe and secure with when, and how, eating plans are to be implemented. Trying to challenge or change too much too soon will cause Edi to bolt, and fast. Remember, to the sufferer, you are 'trifling' with their safety blanket and 'messing' with their emotional crutch and dearest confidante. Concrete eating plans are particularly important when medical risk is high and treatment is stuck. Given Edi's state of health, you may have grand plans but Edi certainly will not.

The overall aim is to get to a healthy weight. The world of scientific evidence indicates that for recovery to occur it is essential for people to return to the normal weight range. This has been put into the Clinical Guidelines for good practice in the management of anorexia nervosa. This is a return to a BMI of between 19.5kg/m² and 25kg/m². This is because it:

- Reduces the relapse risk

- Lowers short- and long-term complications

- Lowers the risk of onset binge eating

- Reduces the alteration in brain chemistry that causes impulsive behaviours, self-harm, etc.

- Reduces the alteration in brain chemistry that causes competitive, aggressive behaviours, irritability, etc.

- Reduces the alteration in brain chemistry that causes over-activity, etc.

Without weight gain it may be impossible for Edi to refrain from anorexia-linked behaviours (social isolation, difficulty with emotional processing, and rigid and sad thinking). If Edi continues to play by AN rules rather than reaching a state of normal physiology and biology they will remain trapped within the abnormal processes that happen when people are starving and stressed.

Progress may be slow. You know you are starting to make progress once Edi's hands and feet are warmer. The following text gives you some pointers of how and what to discuss when planning with Edi.

(a) Naming and shaming rules: Ask Edi to walk you through what it would be like for a full day in his or her life if she or he were to take more responsibility for his or her own nutritional health. Additionally, introduce the concept of gradually loosening, through 'naming and shaming', any eating disorder-bound rules Edi religiously follows (see pp. 125–126 of this chapter for examples). Edi will probably be reluctant to discuss these rules –

being of a highly personal nature. Additionally, Edi will be acutely conscious of ridicule and embarrassment and sceptical of any benefit disclosure may bring. Encourage Edi by emphasising the 'naming and shaming' aspect of the exercise. Remind him or her that you can be there to offer support through the action of breaking the rule/ritual and the consequent anxiety.

Here is how the conversation might go:

> 'Now I want you to walk me through what a day in your life would be like with you taking more responsibility for your health. I want you to go through it as if you're constructing a story board for a film with every action visualised in your mind and talked through in plans with me. Let's start with getting up . . . Let's move on to breakfast.'
>
> 'People with an eating disorder usually have lots of rules about eating. Can you tell me about any rules you might have?'
>
> 'It will be terrifying for you to shift any of those rules. Which would take the least amount of courage to try to break?'

You could then have a discussion about how these rules could be gradually shifted. It may be helpful to rank the rules and work on breaking the minor ones at first, going on to the major ones later.

(b) Targeting Safety Behaviours: It may also be helpful to broach a conversation about safety behaviours (p. 126 of this chapter), i.e. the soothing strategies or neutralising thoughts used to calm and reassure Edi if they have been forced to eat because of social cues, for example to please you. Your aim would be to help them modify these thoughts into something more adaptive.

> 'You probably have your own way of soothing yourself if you feel forced to break your own rules by someone else. Can you please tell me how you manage this?'

'It is a common problem to be so focused on detail that you cannot see the bigger picture, i.e. can't see the wood for the trees. How could you adapt your rule system so that you could take the broader view?'

(2) Planning – a Written Plan for Change

Develop a clear plan for change by writing down the headings and decisions in Table 11.1 on a piece of paper. Any eating disorder rules and/or safety behaviours that Edi discloses and wishes to challenge can also be documented.

TABLE 11.1 Change Plan for Eating

The changes I want to make in regard to my nutritional health are:	
The most important reasons why I want to make these changes are:	
The steps I plan to take in changing are:	
The ways other people can help me are:	Person: Possible ways to help:
I will know that my plan is working if:	
Some things that could interfere with my plans are:	

It is helpful if these plans can set down ideas about all 'hot' areas relating to food, such as meals, shopping and preparing food. The above structure aims to 'walk through' each scenario in detail. Talk about the changes, what needs to happen to implement them, what help will be needed, who may be able to help and then write them down.

Emphasise to Edi again that:

> 'All living creatures need fuel to continue living, therefore all human beings must eat. Eating is not a choice; we have to eat to live.'

It is vital to **review** and **reflect** with Edi. The written plan for change can be checked later – *outside mealtimes* – for achievements and progress or problems, discussion of what went wrong and why, what has been learnt, and possible adjustments for the future. After the implementation of significant changes, try to work through the following bullet points with Edi:

- What I observed when I undertook change.

- What I can learn and reflect on about my change experiment.

- What I plan to do next time.

Eating Information

The goal is to reverse weight loss by gradually increasing the amount in the diet. This is best done by small meals/snacks regularly spread throughout the day.

- In the first phase (3–7 days) of managing people who fall into the high-risk zone of anorexia nervosa the advice is to aim for a soft diet, e.g. low roughage, invalid-type diet of approximately 30–40kcal/kg/day spaced in small portions throughout the day. The total will be about 1000k calories. In some cases liquid food supplements may be easier to tolerate than normal food.

- The final goal is to aim for a normal diet (approximately 2000kcal–2500kcal or more depending on an individual's size, activity level, metabolic rate, climate, etc.) with supplements to rectify the weight loss. **Approximately an extra 500kcal a day is needed to gain a kilogram in a week** (but this depends on body mass index and exercise level), i.e. 2500kcal–3000kcal per day is needed to restore lost weight. The diet on inpatient units contains about 3000kcal–3500kcal.

- Professionals in the eating disorder field aim for sufferers to increase their weight by 0.5kg/week, on average, when supervised on an outpatient basis and 1kg/week, on average, when under the care of a specialised hospital unit. A general directional trend in weight gain is, however, more important than the minutiae of weekly results.

- To eat the kind of calories required to restore weight loss in a sustained and fairly consistent way is, much to the surprise of most carers, a tall order. The sufferer may require encouragement and/or supervision to limit their activity levels to avoid excess 'energy expediture'.

- To sustain weight gain, sufferers will routinely have to eat three meals (including two desserts) and three snacks a day (dependent on age, sex and BMI). Psychologically, and physically, it is more comfortable for Edi to have food spaced throughout the day. A consistent and disciplined schedule is therefore needed.

- It would be unrealistic to expect a sufferer embarking on a new eating plan, and immensely cautious of change, to alter their eating (pattern, portion size, food types, etc.) radically initially. A regular plan (such as three meals and three snacks) needs to be built up gradually, over a period of weeks, maybe initially introducing Edi to 'half portions' of snacks and smaller, but regularly spaced, meals.

- Some people prefer to have the extra nutrition as a supplement to a normal diet eaten with the rest of the family. This supplement can be dropped when normal weight is regained –

providing reassurance for Edi. The extra nutrition may be taken as prescribed extras such as Caloreen, Fortisip, EnsurePlus, etc. or the sort of nutritional supplements that athletes take. Another option is to add in milkshakes, yogurt-based smoothies, milky drinks, for example Horlicks, etc. Some sufferers prefer the former, being more acceptable to them as a form of medical treatment.

- A multi-vitamin/multi-mineral preparation in the normal adult dose (e.g. Sanatogen Gold (non-NHS), Forceval 1–2 or Seravit capsules) is also recommended. The children's preparations are easier to take as the tablets are smaller.

- Avoid Edi consuming and 'filling up' on large quantities of fruit and vegetables. Some sufferers may have got into the routine of living on just such a diet, which will need to be 'weaned down' gradually. During the weight-gaining phase, fruit and vegetables account for an almost insignificant proportion of total calorific intake and their inclusion is to accustom Edi to a healthy and balanced diet. Therefore, fruit (including bananas) should be considered as 'an extra' and not equivalent to a snack or dessert. Such rules should be outlined clearly to Edi to avoid misunderstandings. Maybe suggest to Edi that she or he may eat no more than one piece of fruit a day in the weight-gaining phase (this could be in addition to two portions of vegetables with lunch, two portions of vegetables with dinner and maybe some fruit content to certain puddings – fruit salad and icecream or apple crumble and custard, for example).

- Additionally, avoid Edi consuming excessive volumes of fluids to 'fill up' or to make post-meal vomiting 'easier'. Encourage Edi to drink no more than 2/3 tumblers (200ml) of water with a meal and one with a snack. Fizzy drinks should preferably be excluded and caffeine should only be drunk in moderation.

- It is sometimes useful to start the process of refeeding with foods that are not terrifying in terms of large or unknown calorie loads. Using snacks between meals which are labelled with nutritional information can allay some of the fear. The goal would be gradually to reduce the need for such tight, restrictive rules.

- *To increase weight at a maximum (but psychologically manageable) rate, the following is a daily plan taken from a typical hospital eating disorders unit. Of course, variations are also suitable and the basic structure can be adapted to suit Edi's needs. The quantity served and the regularity of meals and snacks may have to be built up over a period of weeks:*

> *Breakfast* – 30g–40g of cereal (cornflakes, branflakes, muesli or two Weetabix) with 200ml milk (semi-skimmed or full) AND two slices of medium toast with two margarines/butters (hotel/restaurant-size pre-packaged portions) and two jams/marmalades/honey (again hotel-size portions) OR two slices of toast with peanut butter.

> *Morning snack/Snack 1* – all approximately 200 calories. Examples include: a cereal/cake bar (various kinds), a scone/tea-cake/toast with butter and jam, oatcakes or other biscuits – usually 3–4, a full-fat yogurt, a smoothie, rice pudding, milky drink (latte/Horlicks, etc.), packet of mixed fruit and nuts, etc.

> *Lunch* – a sandwich (two slices of thick bread, butter or mayonnaise, protein filling (tuna mayo, egg mayo, cheese, ham, chicken, etc.) and salad) OR a piece of protein (chicken breast, half a can of oiled tuna, one mackerel fillet, two slices of thick ham, etc.) and a serving of carbohydrate (approximately 4 TABLESPOONS or 2 LARGE SERVING/SLOTTED SPOONS) of rice, couscous or pasta or four new potatoes or one equivalently sized jacket potato or portion of bread. The protein and carbohydrate are to be served with two portions of vegetables. If you picture a dinner plate, try to imagine a portion of protein filling a quarter of the area and a portion of carbohydrate filling a quarter of the area. The remaining plate is for the vegetable portions.

Dessert – a smoothie, milkshake, a serving of crumble and custard, fruit salad and icecream, a slice of sponge cake, etc.

Afternoon snack/Snack 2 – same as above

Dinner – same as lunch above

Dessert – same as above

Evening snack/Snack 3 – same as above.

- It is helpful to have the food for the day planned beforehand in order to remove uncertainty and decision making at times of high stress. Maybe a weekly menu plan could be drawn up and agreed together. It may be important to have a rule such that after a menu for the week has been written, agreed together, and stuck up in the kitchen, for example, then NO alterations are to be made by either Edi or YOURSELF.

- Keep records of achievements in meals and weekly menus/meal plans; this can be brought to review meetings.

The only way to judge whether a plan is adequate is to track the effect that it is having on nutritional risk. (*Remember – weights can be deceptive so medical expertise to measure function is helpful.*)

The final goal is to share meals in a social fashion and for eating to take its place as a way of connecting with others. However, depending on the individual, it may be necessary to work towards this goal in small stages – perhaps you could start off by taking a snack familiar to Edi with you to a café and sharing a coffee together. Then, maybe next time, you could encourage Edi to choose a new snack from a shop when you're out or even one from the café itself.

It is also helpful to plan to eat meals in different places and at different times in order to coach Edi to become more flexible with his or her plans. Maybe initially, choosing a sandwich and a dessert (e.g. something standard like a yogurt or a smoothie) from a supermarket and having a picnic out may be enough for Edi to cope with. Planning meals out before the event may alleviate some of the associated anxiety Edi experiences – look on the internet together for sample menus or visit the restaurant itself with Edi beforehand just to browse through the menu board outside. You could even help him or her make a decision about what to order. With so many chain restaurants in larger towns and cities now, Edi may eventually develop a handful of 'safe' eateries – the menus will be standard between locations and she or he will become familiar with what feels comfortable for them. Also, it is worth remembering that if Edi finds one ingredient in a dish too daunting to cope with on the first visit to a new restaurant, reassure him or her that it is perfectly normal and acceptable to ask the chef to omit the item.

ACTION POINT

You may want to find out more about nutrition and refeeding. There are NICE guidelines specifically on nutrition in addition to the eating disorder guidelines:

- Nutritional guidance for adults (2006): www.nice.org.uk

REFLECTION POINTS

1. *The earlier rule-bound eating behaviours are addressed with discussion and calm, consistent encouragement to motivate towards implementing healthy eating plans, the more likely the eating disorder is to follow a shorter course.*

2. After every step/new change Edi makes, the following reflections are pertinent to discuss together:

   – What I observed when I undertook change.

   – What I can learn and reflect on about my change experiment.

   – What I plan to do next time.

E. Supported Eating

If there are no signs that Edi can ensure his or her nutritional safety, it will be necessary to implement some degree of **supported eating**. The following account is a suggestion and provides ideas for how a home carer could set about this. Ideally, this would be a decision made jointly with Edi in order to avert more restrictive means to safeguard health, such as inpatient treatment or sectioning under the Mental Health Act.

It may be helpful to stress that, as in many other illnesses, it is sometimes necessary to take unpleasant medicine. *Food should be conceptualised as 'medicine' to help Edi recover;* in order to recover health, some medicine may have objectionable side-effects or be difficult to take. It takes personal effort and strength to overcome reluctance.

Skill Set for Supported Eating

Outlined here are the main skills needed for supportive eating. These are the essential items to coach Edi in how to modify rule-driven eating:

1. **Plan the meals beforehand**. If possible spend time visualising what will occur (construct a 'story board'). Then during the meal coaching phrases may be used such as:

   - *'We went through this plan yesterday.'*

   - *'We agreed that we would not change anything during meals.'*

   - *'Remember, we discuss meal plans and goals outside meal-times.'*

   - *'We agreed that our next meeting for discussing meal plans and goals is at . . .'*

   - *'You can write down what you want to say after this meal and bring your notes to the meeting.'*

2. **Set appropriate goals**. You may need to start with a shared snack and build up.

3. **Attainable success**. Nothing is more motivating than success, so remember to start with goals that are attainable. On the other hand, do not set too easy a goal as you will not get a sense of success – discussion and detailed planning are the keys.

   During your discussions, gently point out that if there is a failure to work towards goals or weight gain, then admission or restricted activities may need to be implemented according to medical risk. The goal should be that Edi starts to try a planned activity – *beginning and having a go is more important than finishing.*

4. **Set firm limits and boundaries** (ideally agreed beforehand) and instigate them calmly. Restate these whenever necessary, calmly and consistently, e.g.:

   - *'We agreed this at our discussion meeting. We can discuss this again later, but not now.'*

   For instance, there might be the expectation of *x* kg weight-gain per week.

   - *'You really need to eat the meal.'*
   - *'I am going to sit here and help.'*
   - *'Afterwards we can go somewhere else and talk about why it is so difficult but right now let's just focus on eating.'*
   - *'We are not sticking to plan. Let us see how near the plan we can stay, and discuss it later.'*

5. **Remember – it is as if an 'anorexic minx' is sitting on the chair with Edi, whispering critical and judgemental remarks** – *'You do not deserve to eat – you stupid, fat bitch'* and *'Who are you to think that you are entitled to food?'* and *'You're breaking my rules for eating this'.* You can counteract the 'anorexic minx'

skills-based learning for caring for a loved one

thoughts by showing warmth and love and refraining from expressing criticism and frustration.

The sort of things you might want to do or say include:

- *'Remember it is normal to eat and your body needs it. Everyone requires food as fuel.'*
- *'When you don't eat your metabolism slows down.'*
- *'Food isn't the real problem, it's feelings.'*
- *'Let's not let the eating disorder win.'*

Comforting gestures – a stroke, a hand-hold, distraction by general talk in a relaxing atmosphere – are all helpful.

6. **Remember to give support and praise whenever possible** without sounding patronising by merely saying 'good' or 'well done' as this can seem dismissive. Acknowledge the struggle that has taken place, e.g.:

   - *'I believe in you – I know you can do this.'*
   - *'You are doing so well in your struggle.'*
   - *'I am impressed that you have shown so much courage in overcoming your anorexic thoughts.'*
   - *'You have been brave to stick to plan.'*
   - *'I am impressed with your toughness in sticking to plan.'*
   - *'You are such a strong person – I have so much admiration for you.'*
   - *'It is great that you have been able to be flexible enough to change your rules so that you can care for your health.'*

7. **Help by breaking the task into small sub-tasks**, e.g.:

   - *'We had decided on half an hour for this meal. How about finishing a quarter of the plate in five minutes? Do you want me to let you know when you have one minute of the five left?'*

8. **Do not enter into disagreements at mealtimes** (if necessary agree to put it on the agenda for the next meeting outside mealtimes). Remain *calm, consistent* and kind – no matter how hard it is for carers to watch or try to help, beating the negative and persistent 'anorexic minx' is akin to fighting a war for Edi.

9. **Sidestep any battles by calling on higher authority**, e.g.:

    - *'The hospital/NHS Guidelines state that I should not enter into long discussions about food with you.'*

    - *'You are free to choose whether or not you decide to stick to this plan. Remember though, there is a bottom line in terms of your health.'*

    - *'If you choose not to eat now then it may be that many more freedoms will disappear with hospital care.'*

    - *'My nutritional requirements are different to yours. Nutritional requirements are based on age, weight and sex. In this house, we do not make comparisons about what others eat.'*

10. **Give yourself enough time to allow you to be calm during the meal/snack**: make sure that meals are not interrupted by distractions, the phone, visitors, etc. Recruit others to help you do this task. Do not be afraid to delegate meals or other tasks to others.

11. **Do not give in to an automatic emotional response** when you feel angry or frustrated.

    Anxiety and anger are catching – if you are anxious it will ratchet up Edi's anxiety. Count to ten or take five deep breaths. Imagine yourself as a fly on the wall watching what is going on. Gentle background music may help create and sustain a more peaceful mood. Ask Edi if they have further suggestions for introducing a calming atmosphere.

12. **If you see negative behaviours then state what you see calmly and in first and third person**; give feedback about cheating or

rituals with sensitivity and care to avoid making the person feel shame, humiliation and embarrassment, e.g.:

- *'I can see that you are smearing the butter around the plate. I would like to see you try to overcome that AN behaviour.'*

- *'I can see that you seem to be struggling. Is there anything I can do to help?'*

- *'I can see some custard left in your bowl. I would like you to battle against your anorexic thoughts and scrape the last few spoonfuls out please. It is important that we get into good eating habits.'*

13. **Set goals to ensure that you target both the eating and the safety behaviours**, e.g.:

- *'We agreed that you would spend 30 minutes with me listening to the CD after the meal and then would not visit the bathroom for a minimum of another hour.'*

14. **Ensure that you notice and reflect back on the positive things that you see. If possible, ignore the negative aspects as much as possible. Remember to affirm the process and the challenge of eating by naming specific details, rather than just saying 'Good girl' or something similar when the meal is over, which can sound patronising**, e.g.:

- *'I am impressed with how you've coped. You were able to get back on track after we found there were none of your yogurts in the fridge.'*

- *'Well done. You managed to catch up time after eating your tuna slowly by eating your pasta at a better pace. That's a good improvement.'*

15. **Avoid stepping into safety behavioural loops**: do not give reassurance; control the impulse to take the easy option for the sake of peace.

16. **Have a feedback session afterwards (but not in the period just before or after a meal), where you discuss what worked and what did not work and make new plans.**

managing undereating 163

It is very important to ensure that communication at mealtimes is positive and warm. Try to suppress any critical and hostile comments. This is very difficult – seeing someone playing and toying with food and taking a long time is very irritating and frustrating. It takes the patience of a saint to do this day in, day out, and meal after meal. Maybe there can be a rota of other people to help. Maybe one person in the family is particularly good in this role. (Fathers can often be good at this task as food may not have as much meaning for them.)

TABLE 11.2   Things to Avoid and Things to Say

Things to try not to say. Think of your tone of voice	Things to say calmly
Why haven't you eaten it all?	You told me you would eat it. Please do it – I know you can.
Surely you can eat that last bit?	I know you need support and I know you can do it.
Come on, you have not finished that bit, time is running out and I've got things to do, get on with it.	It is hard but you have the courage within you to do it.
What a waste!	Try hard not to listen to the anorexic minx.
I have spent hours getting that ready!	We need to take steps to improve your nutritional safety.
Think about the children in Africa!	I am not going to get into a debate now. Let's get on with the nutritional treatment.
It's disgusting to see you cut up your food like that!	In the plan we agreed, we said that dinner would last less than 45 minutes. You have 15 minutes left. Can I help, should I heat it up again?
Look at how little you have taken! What do you think you are, a mouse?	That portion size is not big enough. Please can you try again?

F. Halfway Support

As well as directly talking face-to-face, there are many other less intrusive ways to give support. Time, confidence and progress will present new challenges for Edi. Your role as Edi continues into his or her recovery will need to alter. Just think of the Dolphin metaphor: swimming ahead, leading the way and guiding the passage when Edi is helpless; swimming alongside, coaching and giving encouragement, when Edi needs a prop; but, quietly swimming behind, ever present and close at hand, when Edi is making positive progress and gaining independence.

The following are some real examples:

Julie had a BMI of $16kg/m^2$ and was doing some temporary office work during the year off from university because of ill health. She made a plan with her father about what she would eat away from home at the office, and when. They agreed that her father would text her to remind her to eat. Thus at 10.30am, the agreed snack time, her Dad would text her, '*Thinking of you*'. Julie would then text back, '*Done*'. In this way they were able to increase gradually the number of goals set in their plan.

When I was eating lunch or a snack on my own, I found that the 'flashcard' I kept in my purse sometimes helped me get through. On one side of the card, I had written five reasons why I had to eat (both long-term and short-term goals), and, on the other side, both my parents had written words of encouragement. The card was invaluable to me when I lost sight of the future, bringing me back to the reality of how my eating disorder was destroying me. AC

Meanwhile, other sufferers have found talking on the telephone to a sibling, friend or parent, whilst eating alone, a good distraction tool. Or, sometimes, if Edi (or yourself) anticipates a meal or a snack to present a particular challenge (maybe due to the day's events or the timing of eating), writing a few words on a piece of paper and attaching it to the food, before you send Edi off out for the day, may help. For example, '*This is your ticket to freedom and a future' or 'You are so special to all of us – please look after yourself'.*

Samantha lived with her parents and grandparents. When Sam's parents reviewed progress they came to the conclusion that it was not helpful if the entire table joined in instructing her to eat. They decided that one person would be responsible for coaching, using a variety of statements such as: *'Why don't you divide the plate up into four, and plan to eat a quarter in six minutes. Then go on to the next one. I will remind you of the time'* and *'You have done well, and come within that goal. Now let's start on the next one.'* The 'eating' coach would sit next to Sam and quietly guide her, not including others at the table in the conversation. The other adults would try to have a normal conversation, if possible including Sam in plans for non-eating-disorder activities.

This comment was made by another carer about how they overcome procrastination:

'She talks and talks and talks and so eats so slowly. When she's got herself onto a topic, she won't stop and so eventually we have to say, "Okay, sorry, you'd better stop talking love. Dad and I are going to talk while you eat, okay, because otherwise we are going to be here in an hour's time."'

You may want to coach a more flexible way of thinking.

'Let's roll a die to see what extra nutrition we should add to your food today. Let's ascribe a different snack to each of the six numbers.' Or,

'Let's learn how to adapt to life less rigidly. I will put different names of snacks into these envelopes and you can choose them at random.'

---

1. *Starvation is a trap. Starvation prevents the development of brain capacity to make change. Starvation removes the capacity to make wise decisions.*

2. *Where* is the meal to take place?

3. *When* is the meal to take place?

4. *Who* is to be the 'meal coach' at which meal?

5. *Skills needed* by the 'meal coach' are calmness, compassion, consistence, patience and firmness.

6. *Balancing the need to re-nourish with the capability of contemplating change* is a tough challenge.

7. *Society protects and acknowledges* this dilemma with the recognition that the Mental Health Act can be used to safeguard the health of people with eating disorders.

8. *Planning and preparation* through pre- and post-discussion, reflection and analysis of what went well or wasn't so successful, is essential.

Other Information

The husband of a person with an eating disorder has set up the following website, in which he describes what you can do and say to help someone in recovery. He gives good advice on mealtime management: see www.anorexiacarers.co.uk

12

How to help with bingeing and overeating

Eating is essential to life. A fifth of what we eat (i.e. approximately 500kcal) is used to power our brains. The brain therefore has a great deal invested in making sure that we eat enough to meet its needs. Two major aspects of eating control (see Figure 12.1 opposite) in which the brain plays a key part are:

1. The 'body balance control' (Nutrostat), which monitors levels of nutrients and the composition of body parts, adjusting appetite accordingly.
2. The 'Drive' system, which involves learning and memory. This relates to wanting to eat – the desire to eat and the pleasure that results from eating.

Both elements, the Nutrostat and the Drive systems, are disturbed in people with eating disorders. In this chapter on bingeing and overeating, the focus is mainly on conditions where the Drive system is dysfunctional – overwhelming craving to eat occurs even though the metabolic Nutrostat (body balance) is OK.

Bingeing and weight compensation are frequently breakthrough behaviours of starvation or privation with not enough balance of nutrients (i.e. if it results from the Nutrostat system taking control) and pleasurable things in the diet (when the Drive system takes control).

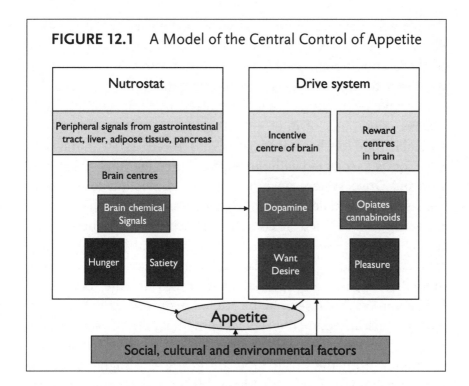

FIGURE 12.1   A Model of the Central Control of Appetite

Understanding Brain Biology Controlling Eating

A great deal of progress has been made in understanding how the brain controls eating from animal research. Persistent, excessive over- or undereating can be produced with certain environmental conditions.

Conditions in which Living Creatures Learn to Overeat and Have Persistent Bingeing

Excessive binge eating in living beings occurs if they have:

- Been undernourished for a period

- Their stomach contents drained after eating

- Irregular access to highly palatable food (uncertain probability)

- Stress.

how to help with bingeing and overeating   **169**

People who develop bulimia nervosa in the early stages of their illness or before the onset within childhood may have had some of these conditions, which can programme the Drive system in the brain to produce a pattern of overeating. Thus if palatable foods have been banned, e.g. no sweets, no chocolate, etc., this creates conditions of intermittent access. Similarly if access to palatable food has been associated with reward and withdrawal of such foods associated with punishment then learning about food with the Drive system becomes disrupted. Dieting to attain an idealised thin female form can trigger an erratic pattern of eating, especially if it is used in combination with extreme behaviours that compensate for overeating. The adolescent brain is particularly at risk for learning unusual habits and behaviours. Studies in animals suggest that persistent changes in the brain and behaviour like those seen in the addictions result if the pattern of eating is disrupted in critical developmental periods. A relapse of bingeing can occur many months later if cues which activate memories from the onset time are given, e.g. highly palatable food. Alcohol, nicotine and addictive drugs activate the same system and animals who have been exposed to an environment that makes them binge become hooked on these as well as food. Thus a persistent anomaly in the incentive-wanting system becomes hardwired. The paradox can be that a desire to be thin can set in train a pattern of disturbed eating which increases the risk for obesity and other addictions.

How to Reset the Reward System

There are many ways to relearn about eating and to re-establish a new balance with the wanting, craving and liking, and pleasure aspects of food. Here are ideas which can retrain the Drive system:

- Eat a regular, healthy, mixed diet.

- Limit exposure to cues of highly palatable (high fat/sugar) or binge foods.

- Eat socially – integrate reward food with that of affiliation and the pleasure of social interaction.

- Keep weight within the normal range (BMI 19–24); the reward mechanisms are oversensitised when people are underweight.

- It is important that the post-ingestive (from the stomach downwards) effects of food are allowed to produce the cascade of neural and hormonal effects that feed back to the brain. This means stopping vomiting/purging. Vomiting means that food does not leave the stomach and enter the small intestine, which is where many gut hormones are released (CCK, ghrelin, pancreatic polypeptide, glucagon, insulin, etc.). These hormones feed back to the brain circuits and reduce the incentive to keep eating. If this does not happen an addictive craving and wanting effect builds up. The taste, smell and flavour of foods experienced in the mouth and nose stimulate the incentive system; if food is in the mouth but not in the gut it disrupts the balance of this system.

- Foods which slow the transit time through the gut and thereby allow time for the release and feedback from these hormone and neural systems to work can be helpful; thus food with a low glycaemic index (check in books or on the web) and high fibre slow transit.

- Introduce a variety of activities that engage the pleasure system of the brain so that pleasure chemicals are released from sources of joy other than food, compulsive exercise, etc.; social interactions or feedback from other sensory systems such as **touch**-body orientated therapies, massage, reflexology, aromatherapy or **sound** and music, or **vision**, such as meditation with slow, deep breathing whilst holding peaceful, pleasant scenes in your mind's eye. All of these activate the left part of the brain, the central soothing system, and act as an antidote to the fight-or-flight threat systems from the right side of the brain.

Your Reaction to Overeating as a Carer

If Edi starts to overeat, following a period of starvation, on the one hand carers may be pleased that at least something is being eaten. On the other hand, these types of behaviours may greatly affect family life even if they are, to a degree, secret. You may be faced with many hassles and irritations. For example, you may come down for breakfast and find that the cupboards are bare. The planning and organisation of your shopping routines may be disrupted. Finances may be badly affected.

It is easy to want to jump to extreme measures to cope. Some strong, extreme, solutions carers have tried include:

- Locking food cupboards and the kitchen

- Banning bingeing in the house.

However, if strategies such as these or others are imposed, they can merely provoke cunning counter-measures and other forms of resistance.

On the Maudsley specialised eating disorder inpatient unit we have found that:

- Such extremes merely 'up the stakes'
- It is better to try to get a negotiated solution
- It is better to have certain rules, consistently applied
- There can be choices about how to get there.

The best way to respond and to help, if you can, is to:

- Try to remain calm
- Try to be moderate yet persistent and consistent in your response.

If you find yourself becoming emotionally aroused:

- Do some calming exercises such as relaxation or count to ten, or

- Withdraw and try again later.

Don't expect instant success:

- Be prepared to repeat calmly what is expected as often as necessary (which may be many times).

Use the assertive positive communication approach in the earlier Chapter 8, 'Communication' to broach discussions on these issues.

An example of how such a conversation might go:

Carer *'I notice that you have been bingeing every day this week. I am concerned about this behaviour. The doctor says it disrupts the normal appetite control system, which makes it difficult for you to get more control over your eating. I would like you to take more care of your nutritional well-being. Do you think you could make a plan to decrease the bingeing? I realise you are the only person who can decide to stop bingeing or not – I'd like to help in any way I can.'*

If someone's basic nutritional health is *reasonable*, the risk in terms of medical danger associated with bingeing is not high. Therefore, where several behaviours, including emotional outbursts, rages, self-harm, are all causing problems for both Edi and the family, usually it is not essential for this behaviour – bingeing – to cease at once; change consolidated over time is a reasonable aim, and many factors need to be taken into consideration when setting priorities for action. There is usually some room for manoeuvre, and discussion of priorities with Edi is always better than anyone else attempting to set them.

At low weight, however, bingeing poses more of a health problem as it can deplete reserves that are low already.

Carer *'I know it's not possible to change everything overnight – is there anything you think I can do to help you reduce your bingeing?'*

Several strategies can help reduce the tendency to binge, for example:

- Avoid shopping for large quantities of food at one time

- Minimise the food stores you hold in stock

- Avoid obtaining large portion sizes of food

- Offer to limit access to cash used to purchase food

- Do not have highly tempting food on display

- Store foods, e.g. cereals, rice, dried fruits, in clear containers on open shelving – it will be immediately obvious when food has disappeared and that thought might just lead to Edi hesitating before a binge, or even finding another distracting activity and resisting altogether; when a binge has taken place, rather than the frustration of planning meals only to find half the packets, etc. are empty, the empty containers on display will alert you to the need for replacement

- Offer advice or suggestions, *with permission.*

Carer *'Do you mind if I mention some of the things I have read . . . suggested that it may be a good idea to . . . Do you think that might work for you?'*

Monitoring and Completing a 'Functional Analysis' (ABC)

- **How often?** One of the main tools to help stop or reduce *any* unacceptable behaviour is first to monitor how often it is happening. You can use a notebook or diary for this process. It is an option that you can encourage Edi to try. You could offer to help review the diary each week *if Edi agrees that such an approach would be helpful rather than being intrusive.*

- **Don't ignore** Rather than ignoring the signs of a binge when you were out, say something such as: '*I noticed signs that suggested you had a binge. Would it be helpful for us to reflect on what happened?*'

- **Don't tell white lies**.

- **ABC** Identify what happens *before* an episode or Antecedent (e.g. Edi feels rejected by a friend who unexpectedly changed plans for an outing) which triggered the Behaviour, and the Consequences, in particular the thoughts and emotions, following a binge.

Record observations in the diary or notebook.

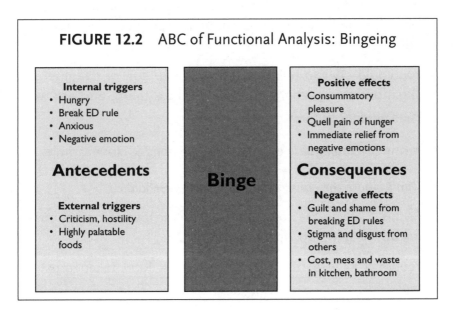

FIGURE 12.2   ABC of Functional Analysis: Bingeing

Internal triggers
- Hungry
- Break ED rule
- Anxious
- Negative emotion

Antecedents

External triggers
- Criticism, hostility
- Highly palatable foods

Binge

Positive effects
- Consummatory pleasure
- Quell pain of hunger
- Immediate relief from negative emotions

Consequences

Negative effects
- Guilt and shame from breaking ED rules
- Stigma and disgust from others
- Cost, mess and waste in kitchen, bathroom

As a carer, you need to think:

- What happens before/after an episode?

- Can I intervene to reduce the antecedents (trigger situations) or can the consequences be modified in any way?

In terms of the **Antecedents**:

- Ensure that there is not free access to large quantities of food. This probably means more frequent shopping for food. Locking away such items in the house can merely increase the sense of deprivation for Edi.

- Another way you can help is by trying to keep the emotional atmosphere warm by spending time together, perhaps suggesting activities which allow time for you and your loved one to spend on shared interests, e.g. doing a jigsaw, tapestry, painting, making a photo collage – especially if doing so gives informal opportunities to talk.

- Remember that forcing or tempting Edi with food items 'forbidden' by the individual eating rules can trigger a binge; even the knowledge that food has been bought and is stored somewhere in the house may be enough to provide temptation for Edi.

- You could offer to talk through with your son or daughter the situations they recognise as stressful for them, and ask what you could do to help.

In terms of **Consequences**, rules may be needed, for example:

- *Don't ignore the consequences for the household.*

- Ensure that you are not colluding with the loss of food by covering up, cleaning up, spending more, etc.

- You may have a rule that says that all food taken must be replaced.

- You may make it clear that you will not be pleased if food for breakfast or for a special occasion is taken.

- You may want to insist that the kitchen is left in the state in which it was found.

- You may want to be clear that you will not supplement and support bingeing by giving money to pay for food.

- You may want a rule about not eating in bedrooms, etc.

These rules may differ depending on individual family circumstances/stage of illness, etc., and may have to be stated and restated many times.

Ideally, as discussed earlier, the rules in your house will be discussed in quiet times outside mealtimes, along with the reasons for those rules, and agreed with all people living at home, rather than made in anger. You will need to think about how realistic it is to try to apply these rules and what the consequences of breaking a particular rule will be.

As much as possible, the emphasis should always be on positive aspects with attention and praise when rules are kept, but with clear consequences if the rules are broken.

Try not to make sanctions which will not or cannot happen, e.g. *If you ever do this again, I'll throw you out!*

None of these strategies will work if they are imposed on Edi – it is always important to stress that it is up to Edi whether she or he wants to change. However, it is also important to stress that Edi show some consideration and respect for others (for instance, leaving enough food for others' breakfasts, cleaning kitchen and bathroom up after bingeing activities).

Looking at the Pros and Cons of Change

People vary as to how motivated they are to change each behaviour and there usually is some hesitation about the idea of change as well as uncertainty about the possibility of carrying any changes through. The 'Risk Rulers' can be useful here, with scores helping to assess what stage of change Edi is at. Depending on the scores, Edi might be prepared to work with you on the pros and cons of giving up each behaviour. The level of motivation can vary from day to day and any positive change may take time to achieve. Take every opportunity to praise wherever possible, and to reassure Edi that you believe they can indeed make the change – a reduction of the frequency of any unwelcome behaviour is an achievement.

If there is a setback, recognise the effort expended and offer to help to try again, perhaps with modified goals.

Realistic Goal Setting

The main aim is to build towards success slowly through small manageable steps, and to consolidate that success, leading to better long-term recovery rather than trying to change everything immediately, overnight.

- Habitual behaviour is tough to change and *any* small reduction in frequency is to be welcomed. Therefore, with all these difficult behaviours with negative consequences, it is important that goals set for change are realistic, not too high with failure a big possibility – *I'll never binge ever again!* On the other hand, if the goal is too easy it may seem to be patronising and boring.

- It is better to start modestly so that change can be reinforced by success.

- Review regularly and reset the goals according to how well things are going – be prepared to change the goals in light of experience and, if you may have contributed to an unsuccessful goal setting, apologise for the error.

For example, on the Maudsley inpatient ward, a policy of totally banning all bingeing proved an impossible task for some people, who would then leave the ward and binge secretly. The policy was changed to allow for one planned binge a day. This was included in the patient's care plan. This policy change and its discussion allowed us to help the patient to explore individual patterns of bingeing and to monitor the behaviour openly, rather than indulging in a cat-and-mouse game. Part of the contract in the care plan was for Edi to monitor thoughts and feelings during a binge. This made it possible for the nurses to help plan other strategies to manage these thoughts and feelings.

It is possible for carers, both professional and family, to work on many of the behaviours in eating disorders in the same way, by developing realistic and achievable plans and strategies for each individual situation.

13

Managing difficult behaviours

Behavioural Priorities

Eating disorders are associated with many difficult symptoms and behaviours. Priority, however, must be given to the need to attain better nutritional health. For most sufferers, this means eating more, or allowing the food to be absorbed by reducing vomiting and/or laxative use. Although some other behaviours – unpredictable rages, disruptive rituals or anxiety-driven disputes – may have a significant impact on others, they are not a danger to life and therefore have a lesser priority than ensuring adequate nourishment.

> My daughter's eating disorder affected everyone in the house. The kitchen would be left in a mess after binges and the bathroom unusable after mealtimes. We often had to call plumbers, at great expense, to sort out blocked toilets and drainage problems. There would be unpredictable, out-of-control rages over trivia – curtains being incorrectly drawn, the 'wrong' cutlery or crockery being used and doors being opened or closed at 'wrong' times. GLS

> D would spend hours in the bathroom, just showering. No one else could get ready. It didn't seem to matter that my husband had to be at work on time or that my other two children needed to leave for school. It caused so many problems that eventually, we actually moved house just to get another bathroom. Fiona, a carer

When Edi is in a less dangerous place regarding nutritional risk, you can work towards negotiation for change in some other areas. We deal with these areas specifically in this chapter; first through elaboration and use of the ABC approach, introduced in Chapter 11, and then through separately tackling exemplar problem behaviours.

Ground Rules

The issue of 'respect' needs to be broached as it is often lacking in the behaviour of adolescents towards their parents in general, but it particularly occurs once an eating disorder develops. Edi needs to be told *calmly and consistently*, and sometimes firmly, that a lack of respect is not acceptable. Although often inconceivable to Edi, she or he is worthy of love, support and respect, and needs to be told so. Everyone else is deserving of this same treatment and Edi must learn to treat others with the same degree of compassion, value and care as they do him or her. All family rules may need to be outlined and discussed, with the reasons for those rules. Perhaps some new rules need to be introduced after discussion so that everyone, including Edi, knows exactly what is expected to ensure that the household continues to function smoothly – working together as a team is a large part of collaborative caring.

Tackling the Antecedents (or Triggers) for Behaviours

Powerful triggers for any eating disorder include **anxiety** and **stress**. Negative emotional responses to behaviours, for example criticism, hostility and bossiness (remember Rhino?), or frequent weeping (Jellyfish?), lead to further stress and arousal in Edi. In turn, these eating disorder behaviours, through a process of positive reinforcement, become grossly entrenched (see Figure 13.1).

In contrast, try to adopt and encourage an atmosphere of warmth, *calmness, consistency* and *compassion* in the house

managing difficult behaviours   **181**

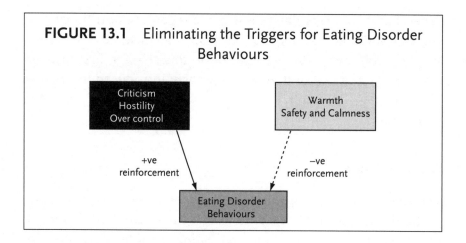

FIGURE 13.1 Eliminating the Triggers for Eating Disorder Behaviours

(Remember Dolphin and St Bernard). By taking such an attitude, through the process of negative reinforcement, eating disorder behaviours can be extinguished (see Figure 13.1). However, such an approach is a challenge – you have your own intense emotional reactions about the illness and its impact to deal with.

Trying to process your own emotional reaction separately, away from the general family arena, can help. At the Maudsley, parents, siblings and other carers are encouraged to have some time away from problems to facilitate this process. Many talk to others not directly involved in Edi's care (friends, carers' groups, and health professionals) to gain some perspective and create distance. Others find a distraction, a hobby, or an outside interest to be an outlet. Such time provides a rare, but important, opportunity to reflect on your feelings and responses to Edi and his or her illness. Additionally, time out has its benefits for Edi – you have renewed energy and can continue to care consistently and effectively in stressful situations. The importance of caring for yourself was introduced in Chapter 5.

REFLECTION POINT

Look at the pattern of behaviours in your family relating to the eating disorder. Could any family member's reaction be inadvertently rewarding Edi's eating disorder behaviours? Or maybe eating disorder behaviours are inadvertently accepted – all too easy to do. Is it possible Edi is getting most attention when she or he makes a fuss about eating, has a tantrum before a meal, or vocalises negative self-ruminations? Perhaps everyone is drawn in, offering reassurance?

We do NOT suggest that you run a 'no tolerance' household and that you move for change of *all* eating disorder behaviours at *all* times. However, it can be helpful to keep a tally of such behaviours and have times of reflection when you focus on change.

You may fall into some of these traps:

- Going into the kitchen when you hear Edi starting to binge and remonstrating with them to stop *(this attention to bingeing can keep the process going)*

- Ignoring the fact that money is stolen from your purse *(removing negative consequences)*

- Disposing of bags of rubbish or vomit *(removing negative consequences)*

- Cleaning up the bathroom or kitchen *(removing negative consequences)*

- Taking the lock off the bathroom door *(encouraging Edi to adopt new secretive and devious behaviours to hide their eating disorder, giving the illness power)*

- Giving Edi the right to sole use of the kitchen or bathroom at certain times *(removing negative consequences; making the eating disorder 'special')*

- Accepting, without comment, that Edi runs up and down the stairs a 100 times after each meal *(removing negative consequences)*

- Accepting, without comment, that there is no food left for breakfast *(removing negative consequences)*

- Joining in prolonged discussions about weight and shape *(giving attention to eating disorder thoughts)*

- Falling into reassurance traps, e.g. *'No, you do not look fat. No you will not have gained an enormous amount of weight with that. No your stomach is not huge' (giving attention and credence to the eating disorder thoughts)*.

In specialist treatment we have found that it is helpful to think of Edi's behaviours and thoughts being driven by two parts:

1. The eating disorder as an enemy or 'anorexic minx' with behaviours that you want to **suppress**

2. The normal part (with non-eating disorder behaviours) that you want to develop, **encourage** and allow to flourish.

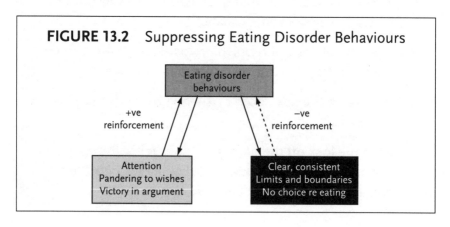

FIGURE 13.2   Suppressing Eating Disorder Behaviours

It is very hard to refrain from entering into dialogue about eating disorder issues and negative self-criticism. Remember that by responding, you are validating and even encouraging Edi to think that such thoughts and beliefs are relevant and have some merit. Try to sidestep getting drawn in:

> 'Expert opinion tells me that I should not get drawn into discussing your rituals with you as it will worsen your eating disorder' or 'It is unhelpful for both of us to discuss food. We will change the subject' or 'I am not willing to enter into discussions about your body shape and size. You know my opinion on the issue.'

If you think it might be useful to have some reflection time, go for the emotion behind the eating disorder symptoms.

> 'It sounds as if you are rather wound up. Do you want to talk about what has been happening?'

Furthermore, to eliminate 'the minx', the importance of setting *clear and consistent rules* cannot be faulted – for example, leaving the bathroom in a mess or stealing money to fund a binge are both totally unacceptable.

Later in this chapter, we discuss in more detail how to work actively on specific safety behaviours (vomiting, over-exercising, or bingeing, self-harm and compulsions).

Rewards in the form of praise and encouragement are needed when non-eating disorder tasks are completed, or when there is an ability to step back from negativity and be flexible, looking at the 'bigger picture'. Edi needs to be aware that you recognise and acknowledge these positive aspects.

Another effective way of promoting 'healthy', non-eating-

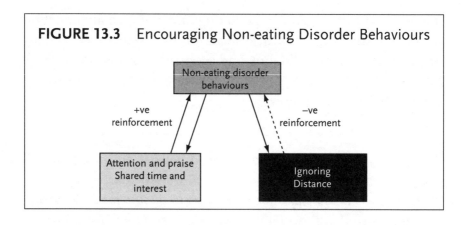

FIGURE 13.3 Encouraging Non-eating Disorder Behaviours

disordered thinking and behaviour is to spend quality, shared, time with Edi. Edi has your attention and life can be glimpsed away from the eating disorder – there's freedom, enjoyment, satisfaction and achievement to be had here too. An aim may be to spend at least an hour a day together sharing an interest or engaged in an activity. It does not just have to be your responsibility. Different family members may like to offer shared walks, TV programmes, conversation, board or card games, puzzles, crafts, etc. Practices such as yoga, t'ai chi, Pilates and meditation offer skills to step back from mind traps, to forget, to relieve anxiety and to 'clear the head'. Finding a local group to join may benefit you as well as Edi.

REFLECTION POINTS

1. Work out ways to stop any possible reinforcement of the eating disorder behaviours.

2. Try to eliminate being locked into thoughts, emotions and behaviours that pander to the eating disorder. Instead, use *calmness, warmth and flexible thinking, with no-nonsense clear expectations* (e.g. living = eating; eating disorder = impaired quality of life).

skills-based learning for caring for a loved one

3. Try to identify any behaviours and situations that have developed at home which need to change. Look for positive strategies to initiate towards addressing these. Set clear boundaries and expectations.

Working on Change in Eating Disorder Behaviours

TASK 1: Using the Spider Diagram to Structure Discussion

As there are so many problem behaviours, sometimes it is difficult to get an overview of the situation. The spider diagram in Figure 13.4, illustrating some of the common symptoms in

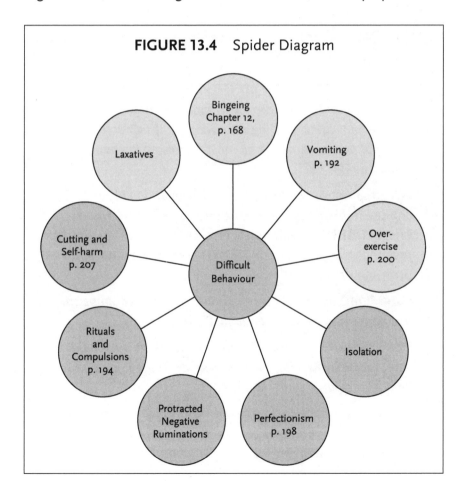

FIGURE 13.4 Spider Diagram

people with eating disorders, might be helpful to introduce into conversation with Edi. The diagram may enable you both to keep in mind a broader picture about Edi's health and not get focused or sidetracked into one domain.

Modify the diagram with blank circles, adding other symptoms or problem areas that are particularly relevant in your home and stage of Edi's illness, e.g. temper tantrums, not eating socially, body checking, etc. For the purposes of this chapter, more information on tackling specific behaviours can be found on the pages indicated in each circle.

ACTION POINT ➤

Carer *'This spider diagram illustrates some of the difficulties that people with an eating disorder face. If I were to ask which of these you would be most interested in changing, what would it be?'*

Let Edi point or respond in some way and explore change in terms of Desire, Ability, Reason and Need. These **'DARN' questions** ascertain the level of readiness reached towards changing a particular behaviour and promote discussion.

Carer *'Can you tell me more about why that would be the one you would like to change first?'* (Desire) or

'You've chosen "Vomiting". How do you think you could work towards reducing this? Is there anything I can do to help you towards this?' (Ability) or

'You've chosen the circle marked "Vomiting" . . . could you help me understand why you feel this is the most important one for you?' (Reason) or

> *'You've chosen "Vomiting" on the diagram . . . Is this because of what Dr . . . said about the salts in your blood and damage to your teeth?'* (Need)

Check whether changing the chosen behaviour meets the **'SMART'** criteria:

- *Is the challenge/change* **Specific?**

- *Is the challenge/change* **Measurable?**

- *Is progress in changing* **Achievable?**

- *Is the challenge/change* **Realistic?**

- *Is the challenge/change possible in a set* **Time?**

The challenge to change the behaviour should be slightly beyond Edi's comfort zone but, nevertheless, perceived as attainable.

TASK 2: Using the Readiness Ruler to Structure Discussion

Once a problem behaviour has been identified by Edi, you can use the 'Readiness Ruler' (first introduced in Chapter 7) to structure a conversation in which you try to elicit **how ready** and **how confident** Edi is to change this behaviour.

ACTION POINT ➤

A useful start may be something like, *'You have not given yourself 0 so there is part of you that wants to change. Can you tell me why you have given yourself 3 and not 0?'*

Such a conversation gives Edi the opportunity to come up with his or her own positive reasons for change. This in turn means that you can step in to give praise, so bolstering Edi's self-esteem and self-confidence to change.

> **Carer** *'It must be hard in the face of your eating disorder to have come up that far from zero. What would help to take you even further up towards 10?'*
>
> **Carer** *'Is there anything that I can do to help you go further in the direction of 10?'*

You could then put your own rating down.

> **Carer** *'Do you mind if I put down a mark on a parallel line to illustrate how important I think it is that you change?'* (Remember to ask permission before you disclose any information or give any advice.)

This might be the basis of the start of a negotiation with some form of compromise.

If the conversation is going well you may want to spend more time on this exercise. Maybe progress to discuss all of the behaviours, in turn, identified by yourself and Edi in the spider diagram. *However, if the reaction is very negative, it is often better to leave the discussion for another time.*

One obstacle to change in Edi is his or her tendency to have unrealistically high expectations in all of life's domains, so setting themselves up for failure from the start, e.g. *'I will stop vomiting and never do it again.'*

Establishing *attainable* goals is vital. For Edi, a positive start combined with feelings of success and progress can be achieved if the easiest problems to change are tackled first. It is irrelevant that these behaviours may be the least important to rectify.

Carer *'It may be a good idea to try to change the things that would be easy to alter initially and later go on to things that are more difficult.'*

Carer *'Do you mind if I say something? The hospital/ doctor suggests that it is helpful to divide things up into small manageable goals. The saying "Nothing succeeds like success" is really true — we all feel good when we succeed at something — and so it is important to set things up so that you can get this as soon as possible. What do you think?'*

When you hear a response indicating an obstructive extreme thinking style, it is helpful if you can nudge Edi into a more realistic response. One way to do this is to calmly *over-state/ over-exaggerate* the response by playing Devil's Advocate in which you reflect their unrealistic ambition.

'So you expect to succeed first time' and *'you're saying that everything will change right away'* or *'you don't believe in "a step at a time".'*

Following these conversations, try to summarise what Edi has said.

Carer *'Let me see if I have got this right you . . .'* or *'I think you are saying . . .'*

Language and Familial Traits

Extreme patterns of thinking, akin to the above, can run in families. Maybe think whether any family member falls into these thinking traps, with unrealistic expectations too. Ask yourself the following questions: *Do **you** focus on detail and lose sight of the bigger picture? Do you have a tendency to be inflexible?* Talking through, with both Edi and other family members, the steps you intend to make to counteract and overcome these extreme dispositions helps. Initiating change in your own thinking style serves as a model for Edi.

Additionally, watch out for any 'catastrophic' thinking; any failure or mistake seeming like a disaster. If you find that your thoughts are peppered with conditional phrases such as *should, would* or *surely*, it makes good sense to try to dampen these down. Such phrases can sound too directive, overbearing and controlling, serving actually to maintain Edi's illness.

Managing Behaviours: *Vomiting*

Figure 13.5 below illustrates some of the **antecedents** and con-

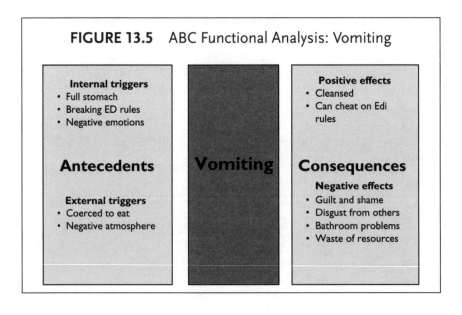

FIGURE 13.5 ABC Functional Analysis: Vomiting

Antecedents

Internal triggers
• Full stomach
• Breaking ED rules
• Negative emotions

External triggers
• Coerced to eat
• Negative atmosphere

Vomiting

Consequences

Positive effects
• Cleansed
• Can cheat on Edi rules

Negative effects
• Guilt and shame
• Disgust from others
• Bathroom problems
• Waste of resources

sequences related to vomiting. Reviewing what you already know, try to think how these could be modified.

Introducing a Discussion

Carer *'I know that you want to empty your stomach after eating, perhaps because it makes you feel safe and less anxious. I worry about how this habit can damage your health and upset your appetite control system. I know that it is up to you whether you change this behaviour or not. I wondered – is there any way I can help you interrupt these behaviours? Or at least increase the length of time you can cope with the urges and not act on them?'*

Strategies to Help

It is always best to introduce changes relating to behaviours after discussion, negotiating rather than imposing change. To reduce vomiting, aim to decrease access to the bathroom or to prolong the time interval between eating and purging for as long as possible. Maybe . . .

- Set and agree on time limits between eating and use of the bathroom with Edi

- Avoid Edi spending time alone after a meal; suggest that Edi phones a friend or you do a joint activity

- Offer post-meal anxiety relief; a backrub, a head massage or foot massage.

Negative Consequences

Do not protect Edi from the consequences of vomiting. If plumbing or cleaning problems with the bathroom arise, discuss such issues, and how they affect other family members, at a meeting. Clearly and calmly ask Edi to deal with the consequences of their behaviour. Acknowledge setbacks and Edi's struggle and ask what might help him or her to win the battle.

Managing Behaviours: Rituals and Compulsions

Compulsive thoughts or behaviours make Edi feel safe by allaying fears and removing the underlying threat. By using the diagram in Figure 13.6, reflect on the situations triggering compulsive rituals and their consequences.

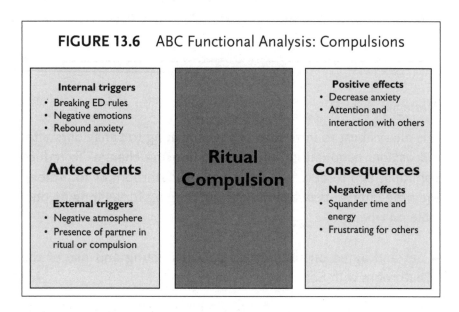

FIGURE 13.6 ABC Functional Analysis: Compulsions

Antecedents

Internal triggers
- Breaking ED rules
- Negative emotions
- Rebound anxiety

External triggers
- Negative atmosphere
- Presence of partner in ritual or compulsion

Ritual Compulsion

Consequences

Positive effects
- Decrease anxiety
- Attention and interaction with others

Negative effects
- Squander time and energy
- Frustrating for others

The Trap

Carers often get sucked into the trap of responding to one of these forms of compulsive behaviour. For example, Edi may ask for reassurance that they have not made a mistake, or that they will not become fat or that they are not ugly, etc. This invites the carer to share in the same thinking pattern, i.e. to endorse the validity of these thoughts. Once reassurance is given, the anxiety decreases – this is rewarding for Edi. Thus Edi is compelled to ask the same question again to get the same 'nice' or pleasurable effect. However, the fall in anxiety is only temporary, with reassurance from others providing only short-term symptom relief and not cure. Therefore, the anxiety re-emerges and the cycle starts again. And again. The compulsive nature of the questions can be very subtle, and involves a shift in responsibility onto the carer with the following strategies:

- Asking the carer if what they will do or have done is safe

- Going over and over a decision

- Refusing to do certain behaviours (e.g. eat) unless a carer is present

- Lengthy discussions about food, calories, weight or shape (i.e. checking details).

The overall goal is for you *not* to get blackmailed or dragged into this 'dance'. In eating disorders, collaborating in avoidance (whether of negative thoughts or negative consequences of behaviour), compulsions and rituals is like giving an alcoholic more drink. The diagram in Figure 13.7 illustrates the advantages of interrupting compulsive behaviours.

Negotiating a Plan to Reduce Compulsive Behaviours – Tips to Success

- Edi should not be treated as if they are entitled to have special privileges (e.g. free sole use of the kitchen or bathroom at all times) to indulge in their compulsive behaviours. Through discussion with the family, agree on reasonable rules.

- It may be helpful to talk through with Edi the behaviour(s) found to cause most anxiety and then draw up a list of each behaviour's allied safety behaviour. Think of strategies to

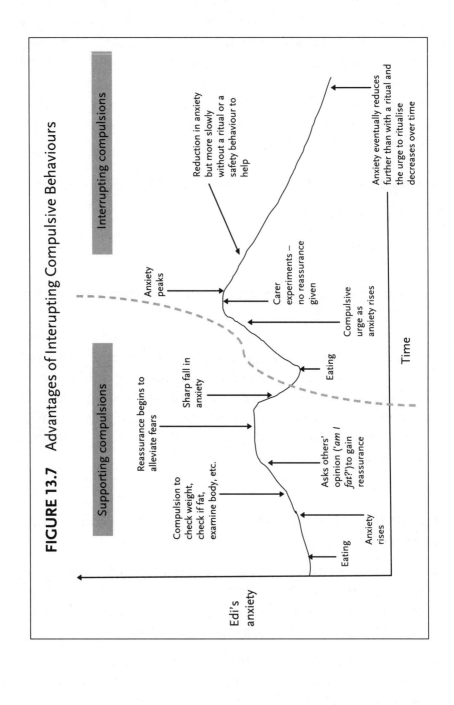

FIGURE 13.7 Advantages of Interrupting Compulsive Behaviours

break/interrupt Edi's compulsions and predict how much anxiety not indulging in each safety behaviour will cause (see Table 13.1 for an example).

TABLE 13.1   Breaking Safety Behaviours

Breaking safety behaviours	Expected anxiety 0–100	Actual anxiety 0–100
Sit for half an hour after a meal	99	
Not check with carer what has been put in meal	95	
Not ask carer if I look fat	92	
Not ask carer if I will carry on eating and not be able to stop	85	
Reduce weighing myself to once a day	80	
Reduce the time I spend checking my body to 30 min per day	75	
Reduce the time I spend on exercise to 60 min per day	75	
Make my exercise less driven and compulsive by sharing part of it with a companion and dog	70	

- Plan for reduction of one problem behaviour at a time, rather than immediate change in every area. Trying to tackle all negative behaviours at once may lead to panic for Edi, and much less possibility of lasting progress.

- Start to target a behaviour that will lead to a moderate rather than high degree of distress to maximise the possibility of successful change. It will be less tough a challenge and any success can be built on.

- Some phrases that you may find to be of use:

> **Carer** *'The doctor/hospital has told me that it is not helpful for me to fall into a reassurance trap with you. It only keeps your high anxiety going. I know you feel anxious now but it will settle on its own.'*
>
> **Carer** *'It is not helpful to you if I allow life in the household to be put on hold because of your rigid routines. It is important for you to learn to be flexible and to be able to adjust to new circumstances. You feel anxious now but it will settle.'*
>
> **Carer** *'This high anxiety you feel now will pass. What could we do to help distract all those anxious thoughts? Would you like to plan for a walk? Or finish the jigsaw? Or . . .?'*

- Discuss more helpful ways to reduce anxiety:

  Gentle physical exercise, e.g. yoga, dance, t'ai chi, Pilates

  Soothing music, pleasurable activities, arts and crafts

  Deep breathing, visualisation, massage, 'pampering' therapies – pedicures/manicures, etc.

Managing Behaviours: Tackling Obsessive Compulsive Symptoms and Perfectionism

People who develop an eating disorder have often displayed compulsive traits in childhood. These may include being some-what stubborn, inflexible, analytical, having to do things in a particular way or the 'right' way and to a very high standard. However, even if such traits were not there before, an eating disorder certainly brings them out.

The form the compulsions take can vary markedly – cleanliness, personal hygiene, tidiness, ordering objects, or habits relating to food preparation, eating and meals. Some of the compulsive behaviours may appear commendable, such as a zealous application to schoolwork, sport, dance or other leisure

skills-based learning for caring for a loved one

activity. Edi may be a high-flying academic achiever, a talented musician, a dedicated sports player and have immense career and professional ambition. Taken too far, these compulsions may serve to reduce high levels of anxiety. Additionally, such beliefs serve to self-deprecate Edi further – they must succeed, they must be top, they must be the best, etc. Failure to be 'perfect' is just one more good reason for being undeserving and unworthy of food and self-care.

Edi lives in fear of failure, of making mistakes, of under-achieving and public criticism. Edi is unable to simply accept that they have done the best job possible with the time and resources available, and that spending even more time, energy and effort may not have led to better results, e.g. it is simply not possible to gain 100 per cent in each and every exam, first place in every race, or score winning goals in every match, gain the lead-role in every play or be the chosen candidate from every job/university inter-view. Edi fails to acknowledge that being human means making mistakes. She or he fails to recognise others have varied talents and abilities and that each and every one of us has personal strengths as well as weaknesses. Our uniqueness makes us who we are and Edi fails to realise that their family and friends love and respect them for being them and not for whom they strive to become.

Edi is unable to accept their error or mistake and just say *'Oh sod it!'* (Professor Bob Palmer from Leicester jokes that people with an eating disorder are missing the *'Oh sod it!'* gene.) The acronym 'SOD' can be used to illustrate how to prevent these traits being taken to unhelpful extremes . . .

• S – Sufficiency

Is this failure/mistake/negative comment, etc. **sufficiently** important to cause this much misery/anxiety/self-criticism in the long-term bigger picture? (*'How much do you think it will matter to you/affect you in seven years' time and how important will it be to you in retrospect?'*)

- **O – Other**

  Are **other** things more important? Do you have **other** priorities? What are they? (*'Is success/praise/achievement, etc. in this more important than . . . your happiness, your health, your future, your family, your friends, etc.?'*)

- **D – Delegate**

  Are others able to help/share responsibility in judging the importance/relevance of this error/mistake/'failure'? (*'May I help to give you some perspective?' 'May I offer you my opinion of the situation/how I see things?'*)

Managing Behaviours: Over-Exercise

Compulsive exercise is a common behaviour, reducing anxiety and producing an impression of safety for Edi. As before, use the following, now-familiar, ABC diagram in Figure 13.8 to identify situations in your own home:

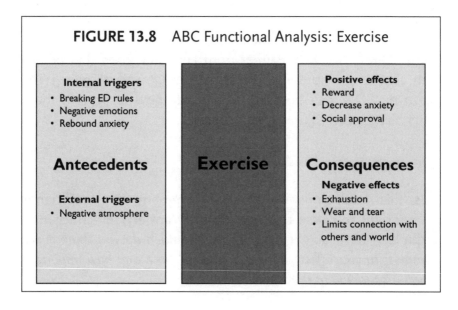

FIGURE 13.8   ABC Functional Analysis: Exercise

Internal triggers
- Breaking ED rules
- Negative emotions
- Rebound anxiety

Antecedents

External triggers
- Negative atmosphere

Exercise

Positive effects
- Reward
- Decrease anxiety
- Social approval

Consequences

Negative effects
- Exhaustion
- Wear and tear
- Limits connection with others and world

Although exercise is usually seen as a healthy behaviour, over-driven exercise in an eating disorder has high costs. In both ano-rexia and bulimia, Edi's nutritional health is compromised; their body has few reserves and is 'out-of-balance'. They may have sig-nificant muscle wasting and weakness, thin bones, disrupted blood sugar levels, a 'fragile' heart and poor fluid and salt balance. By exercising, Edi may be burning valuable resources their body des-perately needs as well as risking both short- and long-term wear and tear, muscle injuries and bone fractures. Additionally, many exercise routines are solitary, isolating activities, e.g. running.

If Edi's health is not severely compromised, rather than an unrealistic total ban on exercise, it may be helpful to change Edi's form of exercise into one with more of a social context, e.g. plan-ning a weekly swim with a friend or joining a dance class. By removing the solitary, competitive and driven aspect of exercise and adding reasonable boundaries and an additional source of pleasure through social connection, Edi may be able to adopt a less fanatical and obsessional view of exercise.

If Edi's nutritional safety is more of an issue, a joint discussion with compromise and a final plan – written or not – needs to be established. An example of this might be if Edi monitors the level of his or her daily exercise using a pedometer or a record of time taken, then works gradually towards reducing this com-pulsive behaviour. Instead of Edi running after dinner each even-ing for half an hour, why not suggest a joint walk for the same length of time?

After emotions have been stifled by the eating disorder, even gentle discussion of such a plan may cause fear and anxiety about change. Remember, 'One step at a time' is again the key, with no sweeping plans to change everything overnight. Patience and time are needed.

Managing Behaviours: Intense Emotions

It is common for people with eating disorders, especially when challenged or attempting recovery, to express intense emotions, even tantrums. These are not easy to manage. They can escalate to severe episodes with violent behaviour involving self-harm or damage to objects or even other people. These outbursts can happen in public and can lead to humiliating displays, impossible to manage.

> The incident at a wedding when my daughter lost her temper, went into a screaming rage when someone made a remark she didn't like, was excruciating – awful for everyone. It caused immense disruption. I've never seen anything like it – she's an only child and we've always had a quiet house. And trying to get her home . . . have you ever tried to get an adult woman in a blind out-of-control rage home? Frances, Carer

Clear house rules about what behaviour is acceptable and what cannot be tolerated are needed. Previous family rules are often disregarded when an eating disorder enters the home.

Each family will have their own 'bottom lines'; rules, whether established or new, to cope with newly developed unacceptable behaviour – and these should be discussed together to ensure that they are applied consistently. For instance:

- Violence, e.g. hitting other people, breaking property, is not allowed

- A display in public will lead to immediate return home

- No swearing or disrespectful behaviour to family members or anyone else

- Respect for other people's needs and property

- If food is wasted it has to be paid for.

The consequences, what happens if rules are broken, need to be clear and to be applied consistently, e.g. grounding, recouping pocket money, etc.

Establishing and re-establishing rules, finding effective sanctions or rewarding activities, applying them consistently on a long-term basis when main carers are exhausted and family members may feel the impact of Edi's negative behaviour on their own life quality, can be a very tough job. The number of rewarding activities is limited, and possible sanctions may also be limited. For instance, in the last rule mentioned about wasted food being replaced, where this is not possible, e.g. if Edi is not working and contributing financially to the household, it will be much more difficult to apply such a rule than if Edi is earning a living.

Finding the balance between being firm and consistent about unacceptable behaviours, and modelling flexibility and not getting bogged down too much in detail, will also be difficult. One thing that is not possible is to ignore the effects of emotional outbursts on family life. The only effective solution is to try to tackle these by identifying ABC, and exploring how the family team may be able to help Edi towards positive change (see Figure 13.9).

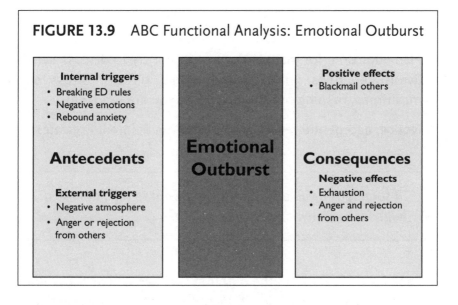

FIGURE 13.9   ABC Functional Analysis: Emotional Outburst

Internal triggers
- Breaking ED rules
- Negative emotions
- Rebound anxiety

Antecedents

External triggers
- Negative atmosphere
- Anger or rejection from others

Emotional Outburst

Positive effects
- Blackmail others

Consequences

Negative effects
- Exhaustion
- Anger and rejection from others

Identifying and Tackling Antecedents

Try, through discussion if possible, to find the triggers for an outburst. Frequent triggers are anger and overwhelming despair. No one has much control over outside events but one way to buffer against these emotional triggers, and to help Edi develop resilience to unexpected setbacks in everyday life, is for the family atmosphere to be as calm and warm as possible. Some tips to help you achieve this goal:

- Caregivers need to have time off. Chapter 5 explains the importance of refreshment and replenishment. Stepping out when the atmosphere is getting tense is also of value:

> *'I need to take a step out as I am getting clouded by my emotional reaction. Let's discuss it in 5 minutes time.'*

- Try to avoid getting trapped into unhelpful patterns of behaviour such as trying to out-argue the eating disorder or depressive thoughts (remember Rhinoceros?).
- Plan your time for interventions – do not try to discuss sensitive issues, rules, goals, changes during times of stress, e.g. mealtimes, rushing out to work, when you are tired, etc.
- Notice, accept and reflect on the emotion before it escalates:

> *'It sounds as if you are upset; do you want to talk, or have a hug? Is there anything I can help with?'*

- Look for the pattern in the outburst – How? When? Why? With whom? (Sometimes Edi will identify one family member who seems to be 'a softer touch' than others.)
- Develop and practise personal statements in advance, to interrupt an incident, so that you can speak calmly when an incident starts, for example:

> *'I think we should discuss this later when we are both calm.'*

Practise repeating the statements, perhaps with a friend or family member, so that they are there when needed.

- Think about how you will manage the first signs of the behaviour by trying to ground Edi into the world around him or her, i.e. by noticing and commenting on aspects of the environment, concentrating on breathing – meditation and mindfulness techniques are useful:

    'It looks as if a wave of anger is coming. Can you put that anger somewhere else in your body?' or *'Can you extract the anger? What does it look like – hot, burning, spiky?'* or *'Maybe you can draw the anger?'*

    'Try to picture yourself somewhere idyllic – describe it to me?'

    'Let's think about what we can hear and feel in the room. I'll start . . . there are birds singing outside and the faint rumble of an aeroplane. I can feel my feet in my shoes and my back on the sofa cushions . . .'

- Comforting Edi during or after the outburst may reinforce the behaviour.

When prevention fails; dealing with the consequent outburst:

- Ensure that you are warm but consistent when handling the behaviour, e.g. *'I love you very much but I don't like it when you . . .'* *'No matter how I love you, this behaviour . . . (name it) is not acceptable. I would not accept it from anyone else and I am not going to accept it from you.'*

- Stay calm and warn firmly, *'Please stop this, we can discuss it later'* or *'We'll discuss this when we are both calm.'*

- If Edi is unable or unwilling to listen, keep repeating your main message calmly: '*I love you, this behaviour (name it: shouting, screaming, hitting, etc.) is not acceptable. I still love you, I don't like the behaviour.*'

- Try to give a more acceptable alternative, and ask how you can help, e.g. '*Please do not shout at me in public, I can see you are cross. When you are able to, I would like you to help me understand what's going on for you.*'

- Offer 'grounding', i.e. aim to shift attention from the emotion onto the environment: '*Put your hand on that wall/tree/stone. Give your frustration to the wall/tree/stone. Think about pouring your frustration into the wall/tree/stone, feel it flowing through your hand and fingers into the wall . . .*'

- Plan for a time after an incident for discussion – what led to the outburst? This may be later the same day or even the next day. Let Edi know that the behaviour was not acceptable and that it will not be ignored or condoned in any way.

- After discussion of the incident, try to end on a positive note, perhaps suggest a pleasant shared activity.

- Start to record incidents in a diary or log book for possible later discussion with a professional or self-help group.

- Do not take the outburst personally or blame yourself. Try to detach yourself from the situation and Edi's emotions.

Case Study

P was 15 and had gradually escalated her food restriction so that she was not eating or drinking at the time of medical assessment. She fell into the high medical risk category and was admitted to an inpatient unit where she started to eat. Her parents were encouraged to come to the inpatient unit at times when they could have a meal with her. Trips home were planned.

However, P's parents reported that as soon as she came home P became preoccupied by her weight and shape, calling herself a *'fat lazy pig'* and making gestures as if to cut off the skin of her abdomen. P also became preoccupied about her need to burn off what she had eaten and when out with her parents would run or power walk. This quickly escalated to P having temper tantrums when she would scream, shout, swear and run off if her behaviours were restricted or forbidden.

After analysing the situation (ABC), P's parents noted that P was calmer in the morning if she started off eating breakfast with them, in a separate room, away from the other patients on the unit. She was less anxious and irritable and not so wound up and preoccupied by the behaviours and eating habits of the others. P's parents made it clear to her that hitting out in temper was not acceptable and neither was running off or swearing. They made clear rules that if this happened they would have to return P from her 'time out' at home back to the unit. They worked together to praise and encourage any control P gained over her behaviour. They thus came to take P from the unit for visits home that started before breakfast, noticing considerable improvements.

Managing Behaviours: Self-harm

Self-harm is often used as a means of expressing intense emotion (anger, hurt, pain, emptiness, abandonment, disconnection, etc.) when these feelings cannot be vocalised or remain unheard or unlistened to. It is as if physical pain is easier to deal with than emotional pain. The sufferer feels an intense release and emotional outpouring following their act of self-harm. They may be unable to communicate their self-revulsion and pain through words; frustration leads them to the act. Some self-harm behaviours are visible, producing increased attention from others, serving only to reinforce and exaggerate them further (a positive consequence).

As with all the behaviours discussed, an ABC analysis is useful towards developing alternative, less risky, strategies to handle the Antecedents (see Figure 13.10); approaching others when feeling distressed, talking and asking for help, finding and using other strategies, such as distraction or relaxation activities, to manage anxiety.

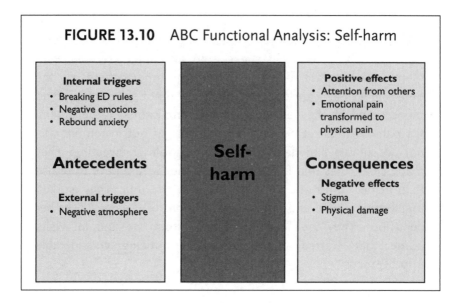

FIGURE 13.10   ABC Functional Analysis: Self-harm

Internal triggers
- Breaking ED rules
- Negative emotions
- Rebound anxiety

Antecedents

External triggers
- Negative atmosphere

Self-harm

Positive effects
- Attention from others
- Emotional pain transformed to physical pain

Consequences

Negative effects
- Stigma
- Physical damage

Feedback

As a carer, you are in a prime position to give on-the-spot feedback to Edi, coaching him or her to adopt behaviours leading towards improved health and a better quality of life. Such coaching requires much patience and commitment but has the advantage of benefiting the wider family in addition to Edi.

Ideally feedback should be given immediately so that it can reinforce and encourage positive behaviours and calmly draw attention to the eating-disordered behaviours ('safety behaviours').

skills-based learning for caring for a loved one

BOX 13.1 Skill Set for Giving Feedback

- **Emphasise the positives**

  Describe your observations clearly, e.g. *'The way you managed that meal was spot on because you were able to . . .'* Also describe the impact of the behaviour on you, e.g *'I was glad that you were able to discuss changes in your exercise plan last night when we sat to review things. As a result we were able to get through the post-meal phase calmly and as planned'* or *'It was great to see that you were able to . . . That meant that . . .'*

- **Emphasise your support**

  e.g. *'I love you very much and I feel worried when I notice that you find it so difficult to retain enough food after a meal, to keep you safe. Is there anything else I can do to help interrupt vomiting next time?'* However, make sure that Edi understands that although you want to help and support in any way possible, the responsibility for changing the behaviour is with Edi – not with you. *'Only you alone can do it, but you can't do it alone – I want to help in any way I can but you're the only one who can really help yourself recover.'*

- **Balance your feedback**

  Describe the problem behaviour you have witnessed in addition to the kind of behaviour you would prefer to see, e.g. *'I love you so much. I can't accept you shouting at me/ slamming doors/screaming. I'd much rather be able to sit down and talk about what has upset you so much. I still love you, it's the behaviour I don't like and can't accept.'*

- **Don't ignore setbacks, calmly acknowledge them**

  Learn from them, plan again for future difficulties and encourage Edi to try again.

- **Stress that it is the behaviour you dislike and can't accept, not the person**

- **Give feedback in private**

  An audience is an unnecessary hindrance.

- **Involve Edi**

  Diagnosing problems, generating solutions, and implementing and reviewing plans should be joint decisions.

- **Avoid criticism**

  'I don't understand. Maybe you weren't making as much effort today. You were doing so well at eating all your snacks without me being there. Why did you throw today's in the bin?'

- **Try to temper perfectionism – setbacks and accidents happen**

  Instead, focus on the bigger picture, what has been learnt and what is important.

- **Acknowledge progress**

  e.g. *'You are really coping well. Two months ago, if you had ordered that same pasta dish, anxiety would have got the better of you. I'm so impressed that you kept your head. The whole family were able to enjoy a special meal out. Thank you for that.'*

  Even if no progress is being made, take notice of, and praise, effort, grit and determination.

REFLECTION POINTS

1. Changing behaviours requires an ABC approach – Antecedents, Behaviours, Consequences.

2. Clear rules and expectations are needed. Discuss these with all family members, review and develop new ones if and when necessary.

3. Analyse ABC in different behaviours, and discuss with Edi and family members.

4. Seek, discuss and plan helpful strategies.

5. Encourage changes with **calmness** and **consistency**.

6. Have time for **compassionate** feedback where you **cherish** any effort to change.

7. Review regularly and plan for the future.

8. Acknowledge setbacks as well as all progress and positive efforts.

References and Further Reading Suggestions

OCD

Veale, D., Wilson, R. *Overcoming obsessive compulsive disorder*. London: Robinson, 2005.

Managing Emotions

Bell, L. *Managing intense emotions and overcoming Self-destructive habits*. Hove: Brunner-Routledge, 2004.
Smith, G. *Anorexia and bulimia in the family*. Chichester, UK: Wiley, 2004.

Self-harm

'Managing deliberate self-harm in young people. CR64: A fact sheet from Royal College of Psychiatrists'. www.rcpsych.ac.uk

MIND, *Understanding self-harm*, a booklet produced by MIND. www.mind.org.uk/Information/Booklets/Understanding/ Understanding+self-harm.htm

'The hurt yourself less workbook'. From National Self Harm Network. www.nshn.co.uk/resources.html

14

Reflection, review – and relaxation

In Summary . . .

It often feels impossible to get interactions with Edi right. You yourself may be tired, hungry, dispirited and emotional, and your reflective resources may be depleted so that you react in the heat of a moment. Alternatively Edi may be particularly tired, hungry, emotional and unreachable. These episodes of getting it wrong can be as useful as the ones that get it right – if you have the courage and reflective capacity to try again.

Reflect and Review

Once the added difficulties in everyday family life caused by a loved one developing an eating disorder are recognised, in addition to working on ways to support Edi effectively, it is important as soon as possible to try to set up a 'Family Forum' to discuss incidents which are causing trouble in family life. While Edi may protest strongly that it is her or his business – what she or he does is their own affair, it is Edi's life, no one else can or should interfere – at the same time the illness is not only affecting Edi's health and future, it is also affecting everyone in the household; therefore it is indeed their business. Whatever happens, working together in open discussion will be the most effective in tackling the 'Divide and Rule' and distorted thinking which is part of an eating disorder, and also in developing effective support in Edi's battle against it. Without that teamwork, it is all too easy for anorexia and bulimia to gain control; once entrenched, without that teamwork it is much more difficult for Edi to fight the compulsive behaviours.

In a specialist ward situation, regular meetings are held to pass on information and support; in a family situation the same is also needed.

A Family Forum – How Often?

A Family Forum, involving everyone in the household plus perhaps any close others who have frequent contact, may most usefully be planned as a regular weekly get-together around a table, sitting around the fire at a convenient relaxed time, any time when everyone is available. The key is **regular** to ensure that everyone has the same picture of what is happening, and also to discuss all other related matters:

- How everyone feels they are coping, with everyone given the opportunity to talk of their feelings.

- Any extra support an individual feels is needed at a particular time.

- What other things are going on in the family – exams, particular work stresses, ill health within the extended family (perhaps grandparents or others who also need extra support).

- Plans for developing constructive rest and recuperation times for every family member – time to start or continue an interest, walk the dog, time out to have a massage, take part in sport, play games.

- Cooperative plans made to enable *everyone* to have that necessary respite time – in teamwork, no one member feels alone, isolated and left to bear the greatest burden of care. While one person – often a mum – may take the role of main carer, siblings, dads, grandparents and other relations, spouses, friends

... all can play an important part in the teamwork crucial to helping Edi.

Building Resilience and Stamina

With eating disorders often following a protracted time span, it is important for families and other carers to recognise the need to find and develop the stamina and resilience to support calmly, consistently and with compassion over a long period of time – not easy in the face of the 'many provocations and annoyances' noted so many years ago by Venables.[1] Look for what you need – and every individual family member may need slightly or greatly different support strategies to enable continued effective caring. (A whole chapter is devoted to Coming Up for Air for carers in *Anorexia and Bulimia in the Family* by Gráinne Smith.[2])

While an annual 'big' holiday may be the highlight of the year for many families, when an eating disorder is part of the picture creating regular breathing spaces – half an hour to share a chat, time to have a meal away from the house, an hour or two to follow a hobby, a night or two away to catch up with sleep, or any other pursuit which gives relaxation – are often the key to survival rather than simply time to relax after work, and longer holidays may be much more difficult to plan and organise around appointments and ongoing support.

Apart from regular Family Forums, *impromptu discussion* of daily progress/problems is also important – grab the moment of calm rational thought and consideration whenever one appears, whether in the kitchen, on the landing, in the garden, on a journey or anywhere else!

Where exchanges have been heated, allow a 'cooling off' period – after which time is set aside for discussion of the incident, what led up to it and the consequences afterwards (ABC), with a review of what is needed for the future. Try to identify any wrong assumptions, misperceptions.

Reflect on Unhelpful Reactions

Carers can help each other reflect on any unhelpful reactions which may be serving to maintain the eating disorder – by acting as a Kangaroo, overprotective and rushing to do what Edi could be responsible for him- or herself and removing the achievement Edi would feel on being able to take that responsibility; or perhaps Rhino, arguing logically against Edi's eating disorder behaviour; or Ostrich who hopes that by ignoring the problems for long enough they might vanish. And reflect on how to achieve a Dolphin and St Bernard approach to support and guide rather than direct and take over.

Working to Help with Some of the Underlying Weaknesses

Avoidance and/or emotional outbursts and rigidity, detail focus, etc. are often core vulnerabilities increasing risk of developing an eating disorder. It is helpful if you notice and acknowledge any steps taken – no matter how small – to change these in the battle against the illness.

- *'I'm impressed you found the courage to tell me what you think about that . . .'*
- *'It can't have been easy to be open about how you feel about . . .'*
- *'I appreciate you explaining your gut reaction to . . .'*
- *'It takes courage to speak from the heart . . .'*
- *'I'm impressed that you have been flexible/adaptable/ versatile/ enough to . . .'*
- *'You've been thoughtful and reflective and . . .'*
- *'You've been courageous/brave/fearless to shift from your safe rituals.'*

skills-based learning for caring for a loved one

Useful Words and Phrases – Which and What?

Carers will develop their own useful phrases for practising – in a mirror, with a friend or family member, to the dog – and using when needed, such as:

> *'I'm sorry, I was tired/cross/irritated/angry because . . . and I shouldn't have . . .' 'I was thinking about our conversation last night. I feel I made a mistake – what I should have said/what I meant was . . .'*

Be specific – and if you can say you feel you got something wrong, it gives the message that *mistakes are OK, everyone makes mistakes*, particularly important as people with eating disorders are terrified of getting it wrong.

I feel sad, angry, frustrated, happy about . . . Carers who express their own feelings, from love to sadness to anger and everything in between, give the strong message that it's OK to talk about, as well as show, our feelings.

All these words are powerful and effective face-to-face, but need not always be spoken directly – texting, telephone, email can also be used. A letter or card may be sent with a loving message, and be treasured.

Repetition

As eating disorders involve a lot of unpredictability with many steps forward and backwards often over a long period, be prepared to repeat what you want to say as often as necessary – *and don't give up because you feel your words have not had the desired effect the first time*. Kind, calm persistence is the key.

Letting Things Be

At times you will find that Edi invites you to pick a fight, or sets up the scene so that you play out the role of his or her own low self-esteem, blaming and criticising. Try to dodge and sidestep these traps – find your own words to say:

'I am curious to know more about what you . . .'

'Thank you for letting me know you feel I got that wrong, please can you tell me more so that I can understand?'

'I am flummoxed and confused about what to do for the best. I need to think more about it, so I want to take a break.'

'I do not want to get into a fight. I would like some time to think, so I am going for a short walk/to my own room now to do that. Can we plan to speak later?'

'It seems as if this is a hot topic. It needs thought. I want to understand it more. I need some time to get perspective. I am going to do some writing around it to get a hold of all the issues. Can we make a plan to get back to it?'

'I have said what I feel, you've told me what you feel; now I think we should both take a break – what would be a good time to talk about it again?'

Be prepared to repeat using slight variations when needed. Remember it is essential that you are calm, compassionate and respectful when you use these phrases, and remember to be aware of your non-verbal expression and your tone.

Reassurance Traps

Endless conversations where you repeat reassurance are harmful. Calmly and compassionately set an agenda with Edi whereby you reduce the amount of reassurance:

'I understand that it is not helpful to lock you into getting reassurance from me. When you ask again, I am going to say, "It is harmful to answer that".'

'It is interesting that you ask me what I feel about your weight loss. I wonder what you feel about it?'

Unacceptable Behaviour

Don't ignore unacceptable behaviour. Practise your own useful phrases so that when an unwelcome negative incident occurs, you're ready to state calmly that this behaviour is unacceptable – *and why.* With so many difficult behaviours you may need to sit back and prioritise what is most important and also what you are confident can be reasonably easy to change.

Outline the rule broken by Edi, why it was agreed in the first place, and what behaviour would be better. *Screaming and shouting is not acceptable. It is upsetting and unnecessary – if you would like the door shut, or left open for any reason, please simply say so quietly.*

View

Think about possible situations when you might need VIEW (Very Important Encouraging Words), and look for positive behaviour to comment on – *I really like it when . . . Thanks for . . .* no matter how small the effort (helping organise laundry, taking out rubbish?) let Edi – and other family members – know it has been noticed and how much it is appreciated. In so many words, express love for Edi, who may feel unloved unless it is expressed. *I love you. I don't like the eating disorder behaviour. I still love you.* Accentuate the positive!

Look for your own Very Important Encouraging Words and phrases, then VIEW and Re-view regularly to find what works best in your own situation.

Consciously bring attention to and stress the positive in any progress towards change. By doing this, carers offer important daily support in the motivation towards the hard work of change for the sufferer. This may at first feel a bit like learning a foreign language – it takes constant practice over time.

Other Positive Adjectives to Use in Change Efforts in Eating Disorders:

Remember that you need to affirm behaviours that are moving to change and not just the outcome. Therefore you need to have on the tip of your tongue a list of adjectives describing what skills are needed to do this, e.g. flexible, courageous, adaptable, resourceful, brave, etc. Make a list (mental or written) of more positive words to add to your list of VIEW for use in your own constructive conversations.

Recording Progress and Setbacks

A journal or diary may be a very useful way of celebrating any progress and success, while acknowledging setbacks and frequency of particular incidents; it may also be useful in discussion with professionals. Such a journal or diary, whether kept daily, weekly or intermittently, may be individual or a collective effort.

A *Collective* Journal?

It is very easy to note only negative aspects in daily life. In a collective effort, with notes added by any family member outlining events, feelings and so on, with each entry – by any member – it can be helpful to develop a system deliberately to stress positives and provide encouragements by trying consciously to balance negatives with positives (no matter how small!). For instance:

> '*Thank you Edi for helping me with my homework.*'   Brother
>
> '*I felt upset when Edi argued about making tea, when we'd already agreed who was cooking and what we were planning to eat.*'   Mum
>
> '*Really enjoyed feeding the birds with you in the garden, and watching the sparrows coming and going. Aren't they funny when they squabble?!*'   Dad
>
> '*Sorry I was rude, Mum, I was getting stressed thinking about eating what we agreed. I love you and really appreciate your support. Dad, it was brill when we stood and watched the baby birds starting to feed from the table with all the others. And glad I could help with your homework, little bro!!*'   Edi
>
> '*I'm sorry I got it wrong when I . . .*'   Sister
>
> '*Mum, I love walking Gem along the river with you to watch the ducks at the bridge.*'   Edi
>
> '*Looking forward to visiting M with you all tomorrow.*'   Mum
>
> '*Thanks for mentioning my appointment – I'd have forgotten about it.*'   Dad

Conclusion

By the end of reading this book you have learnt how important it is to be:

- *Calm*

- *Consistent*

- *Compassionate*

- To *Cherish* and *Coach* your loved one with an eating disorder towards *Confidence*

reflection, review – and relaxation   **221**

and

- To **Care for** yourself and your whole family, by looking for practical solutions and the support needed to follow and Complete the journey alongside Edi on the voyage of recovery.

You will recognise that conversational dances with eating disorders can be unproductive and you will have made changes so that you are **Coaching** your loved one by using:

- **Conversations** with enhanced listening

- **Considering** your heart and head in decision making

- **Clear Communication, Cooperation and Coordination** within your family team to ensure **Consistency** of approach

- **Compensating** for weakness, and storing up strengths within yourself and with your social network

- **Courage** to approach new challenges and **Competency** in problem solving with assertive and appreciative approaches.

With good luck and very best wishes from

Janet Treasure	Gráinne Smith	Anna Crane
(Professional)	*(Family carer)*	*(Personal experience)*

Reference List

1. Venables, J.F. *Guy's Hospital Report 80*, 213–22214. 1–1–1930.
2. Smith, G. *Anorexia and bulimia in the family*. Chichester, UK: Wiley, 2004.

Index

Notes